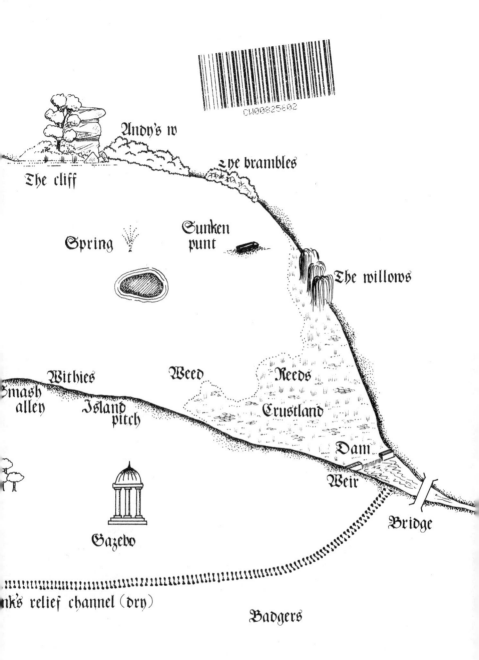

The cliff

Andy's w

ye brambles

Spring

Sunken punt

The willows

Withies

Weed

Reeds

Smash alley

Island pitch

Crustland

Dam

Weir

Gazebo

Bridge

nk's relief channel (dry)

Badgers

Cypry
THE STORY OF A CARP

Cypry
THE STORY OF A CARP

Peter Mohan

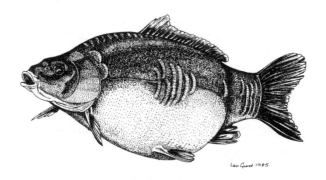

Illustrated by Len Gurd

Beekay Publishers

Other angling titles by Beekay Publishers:

Coarse

Carp Fever by Kevin Maddocks
Success with the Pole by Dickie Carr
Pike Fishing in the 80's by Neville Fickling
Basic Carp Fishing by Peter Mohan
Modern Specimen Hunting by Jim Gibbinson
Fishing for Big Chub by Peter Stone
Top Ten—Tactics for the major species from ten
leading specialist anglers. Edited by Bruce Vaughan
Redmire Pool by Kevin Clifford & Len Arbery
Tactics for Big Pike by Bill Chillingworth
In Pursuit of Carp and Catfish by Kevin Maddocks
The Beekay Guide to Carp Waters
In Pursuit of Predatory Fish by Neville Fickling
Jim Davidson Gets Hooked! by Jim Davidson

Sea

Dinghy Fishing at Sea by Phill Williams & Brian Douglas
Long Range Casting & Fishing Techniques by Paul Kerry
Cod Fishing by John Rawle

Game

The Colour Guide to Fly-tying by Kevin Hyatt
Robson's Guide—Stillwater Trout Flies. An
Alphabetical Survey in Colour by Kenneth Robson

(All titles available direct from Beekay—send for free catalogue)

BEEKAY PUBLISHERS LTD
WITHY POOL
BEDFORD ROAD
HENLOW CAMP
BEDS, SG16 6EA
ENGLAND

© Beekay Publishers 1985
Reprinted 1986

Printed and bound by
Butler & Tanner Ltd, Frome, Somerset

ISBN 0 947674 05 5

My grateful thanks for their help go to my friends and British Carp Study Group and Carp Anglers' Association colleagues Len Gurd of 23 Cemetery Road, Houghton Regis, Dunstable, Beds., who gave up many hours of his spare time to illustrate the book and Kevin Maddocks of Beekay Publishers, who suggested the publication of this edition.

Contents

One *CONCEPTION* 11

Two *BIRTH* 17

Three *FRYHOOD* 23

Four *MATURITY* 32

Five *'DOUBLE'* 42

Six *JOURNEY* 54

Seven *DISCOVERY* 66

Eight *TRAVELLING* 73

Nine *BREAM* 82

Ten *CLIFF* 91

Eleven *TRAP* 99

Twelve *WINTER* 107

Thirteen *'TWENTY'* 114

Fourteen *'THIRTY'* 123

Fifteen *RECORD* 129

Sixteen *IMMORTALITY?* 135

Len Gurd 1985.

In a cool curving world he lies
And ripples with dark ecstasies.
The kind luxurious lapse and steal
Shapes all his universe to feel
And know and be ......

The Fish, by Rupert Brooke

Fish say, they have their Stream and Pond;
But is there anything Beyond?
This life cannot be All, they swear,
For how unpleasant if it were!
One may not doubt that, somehow, Good
Shall come of Water and of Mud;
And, sure, the reverent eye must see
A purpose in Liquidity.

Heaven, by Rupert Brooke

1 Conception

Len Gurd 1985.

The clear lake water was warm and still, with only a few needle bubbles indicating the presence of the many fish beneath that placid surface, on which the early June sun shone relentlessly as it had done for the past ten days in a most un-English manner. The banks were deserted, for the coarse fishing season had not yet started and Bert the bailiff was still furiously at work in his cottage garden, soon to be as lonely and neglected as the lake was at present. Only the two resident kingfishers, a peripatetic heron, the sleepy bank voles and the multitudinous bird population were there to sense what was about to happen in the water.

An almost tangible air of expectancy hung over the lake, seemingly rebounding from the green wall of ancient trees which surrounded the place and which emanated from some invisible but powerful force or emotion beneath the water.

The sun rose higher, the water temperature reached seventy-two degrees in the weedy shallows and all at once the long shapes of fish, silent and purposeful, were swimming steadily towards the shallow water at the edges of the lake. Many of these great fish had been lying torpid in the enervating sun of the exposed lake centre, others had come from the deeps, where the reduced light intensity had encouraged them to increase the level of their activity, a few had found shade under the drooping branches of overhanging trees where the chattering birds gathered, but all now had one intention.

Little three-pounders, experiencing this inexplicable sensation for the first time swam quickly and eagerly in the right direction, guided only by racial memory, while behind came larger relations, some of which, ponderously slow, yet powerfully experienced, retained a knowledge of what was to come born of many years of similar pilgrimages. They came like people to a disaster, from every direction, but with one goal, all feeling alike the excitement of this moment; for it was spawning day for the carp of Cartench Lake.

Only at this time each year was every mature carp in the pond united in intent with its companions by a feeling which it barely understood; only this day a torrent of sensuous awareness would bring each fish to the fertile shallows, to propagate its species in a mass of flying spray. For a few short hours on one or two days of the year and not until the water has been well warmed by the summer sun, the carp come together, shedding their natural caution in the compulsive spawning drive, until they return exhausted to the depths, to rest and regain sanity at last.

Years ago, wise men passed laws to protect the gravid fish by preventing anglers from fishing for them until mid-June, when in their wisdom they decreed that the spawning would be finished. But fish understand no close season bye-laws, and their only calendar is the slowly warming liquid in which they exist. The sensitive nerve endings of the lateral line record their impressions by sending messages to the tiny brain from which results the inevitable action. In cool summers it will be late June or early July before they spawn at all, whilst in some years cold unseasonable weather will persist, the water will never heat sufficiently and the carp will rest sullenly on the bottom, frustrated in their natural desire to increase their numbers.

The milk-white milt will leak unheeded from the vents of the males and the swollen female fish will rub their itching bellies along the weed, yet without shedding the heavy eggs. Slowly, as the fever abates, fish will resume their interrupted feeding and the pounds of unborn eggs will be absorbed into the body weight, until the cycle is repeated in the following year.

There are bleak, barren ponds in Britain where the stranger carp, introduced into these cold northern waters more than five hundred years ago from the teeming heated rivers of central Asia, can never breed, although this is mainly true of the more recently arrived king carp, fresh from Continental experiments to increase their growth rate, than of the wild common carp which the medieval monks knew. Surrounded by hordes of indigenous roach and bream, prolific to the point of idiocy, the great Continental mirrors will live out their long lives unfulfilled, returning at last to the mud in which they feed. Victims of man's increasing interference with Nature, their capacity to adapt to changing conditions bred out of them in exchange for an ability to grow quickly, thus providing more food for landlocked nations, they can never feel the sweet urge of procreation in their new ice-watered homes. Men then wonder where the carp have gone, speaking of miracles, while the flashing silver of the cold water fishes fills the lake with a stunted species, fit only for small boys to catch.

Not at Cartench, though. Protected by the encircling trees from the cruel winds which cool the water, the lake is a prolific breeding ground even for the foreign kings, still not completely acclimatized after many years of residence. Here life is renewed annually, Nature's natural selection ensuring that over-population does not result.

This is the perfect lake, to spawn, as on this day, the perfect carp.

As the fish reach the shallow water, the increased heat of their environment registered at once by the sensitive nervous system lent the final impulse for the act of spawning, and the ritual began. The big hen fish started to twist and turn, backs out of the water at times, strong tails hurling glittering droplets high in the air, frantically ridding themselves of spawn at speed. Beside and below them, sometimes rubbing against their bodies, each female had her half-dozen attendant smaller males swimming continuously around her, covering the eggs with a cloud of white milt which descended through the water like wind-blown mist shredded from the mountain tops and dispersed into the valleys below.

When the eggs reached the weed, where they clung, they were followed tenaciously by the liquid-enshrouded seeds of life, the male sperms wriggling desperately in their attempt to enter an egg and to complete the process of external fertilization. Few succeeded. Hundreds of thousands of eggs are shed by each female carp, but of these only a small percentage will become the progeny of the circling parents. Many of the eggs will never be fertilized; others, as they cling frog-spawn like to the potamogeton or water-crowfoot will be eaten by fish and water birds, or will die of heat, cold, or lack of oxygen. It is to compensate for this that the hen fish carry such enormous quantities of eggs within their bodies; if five tiny carp fry are hatched for each hundred thousand eggs produced then the future of the species is assured.

As the sun climbed higher, the unceasing activity seemed to redouble. Wherever the lake margins were shallow, there the pattern was repeated, the water erupting in a fury of effort. The birds were shocked into silence by the savagery of the smashing tails which flailed the surface into foam, while a solitary grey squirrel busy among the low overhanging branches of an old horse-chestnut, chattered with fright at the first great splash and accelerated into the higher branches where he watched for a minute with his sharp little eyes, before turning away once more to his perennial search for food.

The moorhens and coots, usually so contemptuous of the carp's activities, always ready to race the fish for the pieces of bread crust thrown by cunning anglers, cowered beneath protecting banks, some even leaving the rocking water to waddle confusedly into the trees.

In the late afternoon, a young boy of about fourteen suddenly appeared, breathless, at the end of the track which led to the village. His name was Andrew. He was small, brown-haired and bright-eyed and lived in a cottage near the lake. He was already an aspiring carp angler whose ultimate ambition— his parents said his *only* ambition—was to catch the largest carp that had ever swum, and to catch it from this lake which he loved, and which he had considered 'his' since his father had first brought him here on a roach-fishing expedition four years ago. The boy had since read much carpy literature, learning to take a few small unwary fish in the early summer months, but he knew he had much to learn, which was why he haunted the lake during his every spare moment throughout the year, seeking to share its secrets.

As he strolled casually down the grassy track hands in pockets and whistling tunelessly, he had heard the huge splashing and had broken into a run, wondering what was happening at the water. Reaching the bank, he stopped precipitantly with eyes widening in wonder at the sight. Right in front of him the swirling water was black with the gyrating bodies of the spawning carp as they still concentrated on their pleasurable task, completely oblivious to danger.

Why, I could touch them, thought Andy, so when the next great fish passed uncaring with its long dorsal dividing the surface, he bent forward, arm outstretched, his hand resting momentarily on the back of a carp bigger than he would catch for many years. He knew it weighed over twenty pounds. Unaware, indifferent, the fat hen fish ploughed on through the water, occasionally turning on its side to facilitate the extrusion of the eggs. Soon the boy's shirt and trousers were soaked by the flying water displaced by a myriad broad tails as he leaned closer to watch the cycle of life being renewed before his eyes.

He knew what he was seeing, having read of the commotion caused by breeding carp, but his senses were bemused by the turmoil in that normally placid water, by the loud and continuous smacking noise of the carps' tails as they turned, and by the proximity of fish larger than those which had fed his dreams till now; the scene had for him a kaleidoscopic fascination which he was never to forget, although he saw it repeated many times in the future.

Already passionately interested in natural history in relation to the life which existed in and around the lake, Andy was watching for the first time the actual process of reproduction, third strongest of the passions which animate all wild creatures, and his senses responded with a genuine awe and admiration. Letting his body collapse on to a moss-covered fallen tree trunk, he contemplated the spawning carp until the sun fell away into the west, and the light began to fade.

Shaking their now flaccid stomachs to force out the last remaining trace of the eggs and the milt, the parent carp sank exhausted into deep water, there to rest their tired muscles at the end of a day in which they had contributed compulsively but unknowingly to the immortality of their species; as they did so, others arose to take their place on the spawning grounds, until every mature carp in the lake had taken part in a spectacle unique in Nature by the fury of its noise and effort.

It was amid this confusion, safely jellied inside a protoplasmic capsule, that Cypry was conceived.

2 Birth

Len Gurd 1985.

The name Cypry is derived from *Cyprinus carpio*, Latin name for the common carp. As the mirror and leather carps are but varieties of the same species, then they share the same name even though they are technically 'king' carp whose growth rate has been increased by those selective breeding experiments.

But the carp is not merely the chief member of the huge *Cyprinidae* clan with many other fishes as its cousins; it is the king of the genuine fresh-water fish by virtue of its size and 'intelligence'. Only the pike approaches it in bulk—salmon are after all more than half a sea fish—while in sensitivity and awareness carp are in a class of their own. Other fish are fairly easily deceived, especially game fish like the trout, which, although quick-sighted and fearful, is particularly stupid; because this is so, men often prohibit the use of natural baits, using artificial confections of fur and feather to tempt them. This they call more sporting, knowing in their hearts the true reason being that the trout will almost invariably take a worm placed near them, thus making them too easy to catch without the introduction of some unnatural difficulty.

The reverse is true of carp. Its natural foods are generally too small to be used as baits, and a worm placed near it, while being a favourite food, will cause it to swim away more often than not, out of natural caution. No bait bans are needed here; even with every possible edible substance and flavour at his disposal as bait, the carp angler will find it very hard to trap the big fish once they have learnt by bitter experience the feeling of a hook in their mouths and the suffocating sensation of the air which they cannot breathe.

As for size, the official record rod-caught carp of 44 pounds is one of the largest fish of any fresh-water species to be caught in England, while it is well-known that in certain well-hidden lakes live carp well in excess of this size, reaching perhaps as much as seventy or eighty pounds...

Cypry, the carp conceived at Cartench, would one day be greater than them all.

When Andy, the boy, left the waterside after that exciting day, his mind full of huge fishy shapes amid turbulent waters, he passed the cottage of Bert Brimmacombe, the bailiff, on his way home.

'Mr Brimmacombe,' he called over the garden wall, 'I've seen the carp spawning!'

Bert, a wiry, weather-beaten, taciturn man, who was a first-class guardian of the lake because he steered clear of friendship with anyone who fished or lived near it, and because he interpreted all instructions given to him quite literally, had a lot of time for this boy, whom he recognized as a kindred spirit in a way, loving the lake and its population as much as he did himself. He would never do anything to harm them, unlike most of them damned anglers, he said to himself. Straightening up from the garden where he had laboured all day, knowing that it would get little of his attention once the fishing season began in a week's time, Bert replied:

'At it today was they? Oi thought 'twas about toime. Vine sight, bean't it, Andy?'

'Fabulous,' said the boy, his eyes shining.

'I'll never forget it, never. All those huge fish....' His voice tailed off as he remembered. The man nodded.

'Reckon y' never will, b'y. Watch 'un again in ten days or zo. Be 'atchin' then, her will.'

He bent again to his work. Andy wandered dreamily off home to the inevitable scolding. Ten days; he'd be there every day waiting for the tiny fish to appear!

At the lake, all was quiet and normal. The water-birds shunted busily over the water, some eating the long strings of eggs which they had soon discovered among the weed. Shrews and field-mice fed frenetically on the grassy banks, and a great grey heron stood immobile but frighteningly alert in the shallows, waiting for his dinner to swim by. His competitors the kingfishers, with a late brood of three young to feed in a smelly fish-bone nest among a tangle of undergrowth in a corner of the lake, sat and dived alternately, rarely failing to come up with a small roach in their beaks, their rapid, colourful movements contrasting oddly with the camouflaged apparent immobility of the tall heron, as efficient a fish-catching machine as they in his way, although less extrovert.

The wood was full of noise and movement. There was the constant meaningless calls of many birds, overlaid occasionally by the screech of the jay, the warning note of an alarmed blackbird, or the two-toned signal of a hen pheasant. There were the footsteps of the birds amongst the remains of last year's leaves which still carpeted the ground in places, the knocking of the branches as squirrels leapt from one to another leaving them swinging behind, and the light whistle of the wind through the tree trunks. Yesterday's disturbance was already forgotten; while life developed silently among the carp eggs, the everyday activities of the animals, checked by the shock of the carp commotion, now resumed as usual.

Beneath the water, deeply hidden, the resting fish lay still. Soon their metabolisms, disturbed by the spawning cycle which had precluded much serious feeding for the few days immediately before the great day, would return to normal, they would feel hunger and start to search in the mud of the bottom for the bloodworms, water snails, shrimps, larvae, and zoo-plankton which made up their staple diet, in which the ground-bait of anglers now played a big part.

Meanwhile, black-barred perch, colours glowing, accompanied by the small marauding pike, menacing and toothy among the twining water weeds, had found the tasty eggs, and were avidly devouring them. Long sinister eels awaited the night before taking their share of this annual manna provided by the unknowing carp; even had they known, they would not have cared. Eggs shed and fertilized, their job was done, until the fever grew in them again. The carp spawn was alone, unprotected by parental care; birds guard their eggs, mammals protect their young, but the fishes' instinct is only for procreation.

By this time of the year, most of the animals in the wood surrounding the lake had reared their young, although the badger cubs in the big sett on the high ground at the south end were still too helpless to fend for themselves and the local farmer had dug out two litters of fox cubs from different earths nearby, killing the little snapping creatures quickly with a sense of satisfaction as he thought of the chickens they might have killed. Only the fish were left to hatch, apart from the second broods of some of the birds, and as the long summer days passed, interspersed with light showers which drove oxygen into the water, enlivening the fish, life grew inside the miniscule black nucleii of the surviving eggs.

Seven days after the carp had spawned, the anglers came. Shortly before midnight on June 15th, silent carp fishers loaded down with their heavy tackle, selected their pitches with jealous glances around at others already better placed, prepared their gear, and settled down to await the first joyful minute of the new season. Many would miss work the next day, some with permission, others with spurious illnesses. There are many anglers who never fail to fish this first day; some travel hundreds of miles to their favourite waters to cast in on the stroke of midnight, hopeful as ever that this year they will catch their biggest fish.

As each one arrived, a small figure materialized alarmingly at his side; it was the bailiff, whose astonishing woodcraft had been learnt, it was said, in years of poaching when he was younger, although this could not be proved, as he was never caught. Now Bert was on the side of the law; each angler had to produce his club membership card and his River Authority licence. Without it, he would be sent home, cursing, barred from fishing until he could show his permits to the bailiff.

There was good reason for such strictness. The lake, the woods, the land behind the woods, the farms and most of the village belonged to Major James Wyatt-Smythe, whose fortified fifteenth-century manor house set on a hill, dominated the neighbourhood physically as the Wyatt-Smythe family had done financially and practically for over five hundred years. A stern but fair man, still referred to as 'Squire' by the older generation, most of whom held their black and white timbered houses, gathered as if for shelter round the fine Norman church, at a low rent from the Estate, the Major leased the fishing to the local club at a peppercorn rent. His stipulations were:—No night fishing (except on opening night from midnight), no litter, no vandalism and no poaching, which included fishing without a permit. Knowing they would lose one of the finest and most beautiful fishing lakes in the country if the owner had cause for complaint, the club committee had made other, more stringent, rules.

Small boys could not fish if unaccompanied by adults—the rule that was most often broken! Fires, dogs, transistor radios, and guns were banned, and picnicking was not allowed. The club secretary instructed Bert to enforce these rules, which he did down to the last detail. This was a water for serious, well-behaved anglers, not for those who wanted a bit of fishing, combined with some larking around if things were slow. The bailiff's word was law, sensible members kept on the right side of him, so trouble at the lake was rare.

After the first wave of carp fishers had cast in at midnight, to place their rods in the forked rests, switch on their electric bite indicators, and settle hopefully on their bed-chairs, each an oasis of hope in the darkness, Bert could retire to his cottage for a short night's sleep, knowing that the next lot of anglers, the tench and bream men, were unlikely to arrive until dawn. By six a.m. he would be there again, appearing and disappearing like the wraith of one of the long dead monks from the ruined monastery near the north end of the lake.

Oblivious to the successes and disappointments of the anglers, still secure in their encompassing jellied world, the embryo carp began to move. Tiny black wriggling specks became miniature fish as they ate the surrounding material, substitute for a mother's milk, from the inside at first. Then, ten days after they had left the bodies of their parents, and three from the time of the anglers' arrival, the carp began to hatch.

In a thick bed of potamogeton, exactly opposite where Andy had stood entranced, staring at the great fish, the first tiny carp

fry pushed its impatient way through the remains of the protoplasm into its own element. It contorted its quarter-inch body,
perfect in every detail, into position, and began to eat the last
traces of the womb-food.

Cypry the carp was born.

3 Fryhood

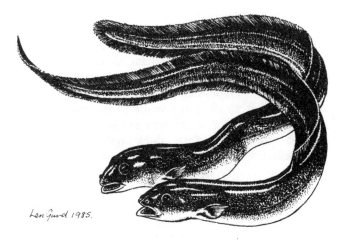

Len Gurd 1985.

At first, the little fish stayed close to its birth-place, as if
unaware of its great new universe. The immeasurable curving
liquidity of this fluid world was beyond its comprehension;
every shape and shadow seemed an enemy, while the bewilder-
ing chiaroscuro of varying light intensities among the huge
intertwined weed stems was menacing in its lack of stability.
Each movement of water-bird or fish sent warning vibrations
through the water to be recorded by the rudimentary inexperienced nervous system and brain of the baby carp. Unable
to sort out the confused messages, terrified by each fresh
impression, alone in the immensity of water-space, Cypry fled
into the green weed jungle every few seconds, there to hang
quiveringly alert, ready to react instantaneously to any sudden
danger. There he remained for a minute or two, until the
hunger instinct overcame his fear, the tiny fins flickered and
he progressed by means of a series of darts and dashes back
to the fast disappearing protoplasm which was the only home
he was ever to know.

The carp fry had every good reason for his fears. All about
him were enemies; predatory pike and perch, always searching for an easy meal, enormous writhing eels, night hunters
supreme, whose silent, sinuous approach gave no warning,

until with astonishing speed their lethal jaws crushed the unsuspecting victim. Feared and hated by fish and men alike, preferring dead or stationary food but taking anything it can catch to assuage the insatiable carnivorous appetite, the snake-like mysterious eel, altered in both shape and character by the trauma of its birth and the fantastic Atlantic crossing to its freshwater home, lives out its friendless life despised and alone until it too makes that suicidal journey from which it will never return. The inhabitants of the lake, sensing the alien strangeness, avoid it at all times, while to the carp fry the eel is an unimagined monster, a chimera of the dark.

Above the reflecting surface, duck, dabchick, and diving streamlined kingfisher will catch the carp if it can, the spear-like beak of the hungry heron will tear it from its element, and the monstrous white neck of the graceful swan, deranged by its own beauty, madness betrayed by the ever-angry eyes, reaches occasionally for fishy food as a change from watery weed. Man is the lesser but ever-present enemy, controlling the environment as he does, capable of draining, netting, or filling the lake for his own selfish reasons, to kill, if not by intent, by indifference.

The fry have no allies. No parent, brother, sister, or friend to stand by them in the extremities of danger. Only through the obscurity of the element, the helpful if uncaring water weed, their own insignificance and quickness, and the rapidity of their reactions, will they survive to maturity.

Cypry's first few weeks of life were an inextricable mixture of fear and feeding. By the time the jelly was gone, he had learnt to siphon microscopic insects, zoo-plankton, and daphnia from the life-giving water which flowed continually through his mouth and out by the oxygen-extracting gill-rakers. The weed was full of these tiny creatures, so it was here, mostly in mid-water, that Cypry lived and fed. Later he was aware of others, similar in size and shape to himself, foraging among the water plants; these were not enemies, he recognized, but merely competitors for the plentiful food which sur-rounded them. For tribal reasons, the little carp soon joined in a shoal to feed. There was less safety in this concentration, but some amorphous feeling of belonging and companion-ship led them to shoal in this illogical way. Any immediate threat sent them scattering into the sheltering weed like ants from a disturbed ant-hill, alone once more with their fear. The less quick were caught and disappeared permanently, eaten by the teeth, jaws, and thrusting yellow beaks which appeared amongst them so terribly, monstrous masters of their world, demanding instant sacrifice to that immutable water-law : whatever lives is food for others.

As with all masters, they taught. Through fear the tiny carp began to learn lessons which for the aptest pupils would ensure survival. Carp have an ability for learning well in advance of other fish. Not to be confused with true intelligence or powers of reasoning, this aptitude for learning singles out the carp from lesser fish, making them harder to catch, more of a challenge to the angler, and so more interesting to study.

Humans, even those born of the same mother, vary considerably in intelligence and ability. The same is true of animals, and of fish. Experiments with marked carp have proved that one fish will be caught again and again, while another will learn rapidly from the traumatic experience, treating future offerings with caution, thus being taken less frequently. These 'more intelligent' fish grow faster than the others, too, their alertness leading them to find food more easily than their shoal-mates, as well as avoiding danger more successfully. As any fishery-owner knows, carp hatched or introduced at the same size and age have very uneven rates of growth for this reason, the 'clever' fish reaching perhaps thirty pounds in weight before their companions are little more than half this size.

Cypry soon stood out in this way, like a brilliant scholar in a class of dullards. He was always the first to see danger, and when he saw it, his ultra-quick reactions, combined with an extra power of acceleration, enabled him to take violent evasive action ahead of the others, to lie unmoving in the thickest weed until the threat was past, when he would emerge, dartingly, to recommence feeding while the rest were still recovering from their shock. By August he weighed seven ounces and was noticeably larger than any other fish in the shoal. He was now accepted as the leader as is the way with fishes, a position he adopted with ever-growing confidence, swimming ahead of the rest as the biggest often do, signalling danger or food to the shoal by the movements of an already powerful body.

Not all was fear and food in fryhood. Hunger satisfied, monsters exorcized, the young carp would chase each other endlessly through the waving weed-stems, feeling the ecstatic joy of an increasing mastery of the liquid in which they lived as it flowed caressingly over their mucus-covered scales in perpetual motion. Warmth they loved, perhaps with racial memories of their long-dead ancestors' homes in climates where the water was ever warm; whenever the summer sun shone, they would play in the hot surface layer of the lake, or lie basking in a trance of happiness under the heated lily-pads, heedless for a short time of the ceaseless struggle for survival. Sometimes they flung their contorted bodies into the air from pure *joie de vivre*, wondering at the cold, bright, reversed world which revolved about them for an instant, until with a pleasurable shock they fell safely back into reality.

In early autumn, Cypry found out more about the world beyond. It was a cool windy day, with water temperatures beginning to drop towards winter levels. Dead brown leaves were falling from the trees into the water, where they were blown along the surface like shrunken charred Viking funeral boats, until they became sodden and sank to the bottom, to join the decaying mass collected there over the centuries. Migratory birds had already left for warmer lands, squirrels ranged restlessly through the wood, seeking suitable food for their winter hoards and fewer anglers came to the pool ...

Ever hopeful small boys continued to fish, hauling young roach from the water, to be thrown carelessly into keep nets where they flung themselves ceaselessly at the meshes in a vain attempt to escape. It was not the fault of the youngsters that they treated their catch badly; they were but emulating many of their elders, most of whom knew no better themselves. It is true that a fish has no highly developed nervous system in its mouth, and so can feel no pain from the angler's hook. The choking sensation induced by air instead of water breathing does little harm provided it does not last too long, but the burn of a hot, dry gripping hand can hurt, while constant battering against the meshes of a keep net can damage sensitive tissue irretrievably. The good angler strikes, to hook the fish in the lip only, then lifts the fish with wet hands, returning it swiftly to the water, where it is supported upright until it gains sufficient strength to swim away. Never will the fish be 'thrown back', to suffer internal injuries from the unexpected impact. Treated with consideration, the fish will soon resume feeding; they have been caught in this way several times on the same day, so proving that the experience, although possibly mildly traumatic, is not seriously damaging. The boys knew nothing of this; they just enjoyed catching the fish, their sport a relic of the essential food-hunting activities of their primitive forebears.

It was one of these boys who caught Cypry. Feeding avidly, he had sucked in a couple of white, juicy-looking maggots, then had turned to look for more. As he did so, he felt pressure at his mouth. Cypry shook his head, not yet alarmed, but the feeling persisted unpleasantly, increasing in force until he knew that there had been something wrong with those tempting maggots. Using all the latent power in his three-quarter pound body, the carp bolted for the shelter of the nearest friendly weed bed. The unseen enemy was too strong for him, however. He felt himself being pulled through the water away from the weed, to be ejected into the suffocating air, then deposited roughly on to a hard surface. His eyes glazed, unable to get sufficient oxygen, he flapped and wriggled among the triumphant shouting boys while the hard hook was forced from his mouth, tearing some of his flesh as the barb was released. The gripping hands touched and held him, then he was thrown unceremoniously back into the water. Thankfully, the carp righted itself, sucked in the life-giving oxygen, shook itself to recover from the shock of landing, and started to swim away; impossibly, it was unable to do so. The net was a prison, and he swam inside, as a dozen little roach thrashed against his sides. Cypry hated the trapped feeling more than the rough handling from which his strong young body would soon recover. Accustomed to the freedom of the lake, he felt disorientated, frustrated, and afraid as he crashed furiously against the side of the yielding but unbreakable net.

On the bank, the boys were jubilant. This was their first carp, and how it had fought! Then an older boy, who had watched them frowningly from a distance, came up to them. It was Andy.

'Carp, wasn't it?' he enquired with apparent casualness.

'Cor, yes, didn't 'alf fight and all. Pound and an 'alf, at least,' boasted the young captor.

Andy hesitated, then made up his mind. He had never lacked moral courage.

'Put it back,' he said quietly. 'Now. Don't you know that it hurts fish to keep them in nets? That carp may one day be a twenty pounder, if you don't kill it. Put it back, or I'll tell the bailiff.'

Expostulating incredulously, but afraid of the threat, the lads lifted the net from the water, and Andy saw Cypry for the first time. His wet hands quickly separated the carp from the twitching silver roach, then lowered it gently into the water where it shot off out of sight at once. Andy sighed, trying to explain to the younger children that there were only a couple of hundred of the carp in the lake, compared with perhaps fifty thousand roach, so each fish was valuable. They watched him resentfully, calling a few filthy words at his back as he walked away, saddened by the conviction that they would grow up as heedless and ignorant of the fish they caught as most occasional anglers do. Serious carp anglers fish for sport alone, returning their catches unharmed to grow bigger, unlike the trout and salmon men who fish to kill.

Andy himself had fished hard that summer, but with very little success. Almost every evening, and sometimes all Saturday night when he could get his parents' permission, he was at the water, either trying to catch the larger carp, or closely watching older carp specialists, as eager to learn as to catch fish. So far his best carp had weighed only six pounds—an enormous fish compared with the little roach and bream taken by most of his contemporaries, but small, he knew, by carp-fishers' standards. The few experienced men who would spare the time to talk to a young boy had convinced him that anything of under ten pounds was of little account in the carp fishing world; fish of above this weight were invariably referred to as 'doubles' for obvious reasons, so he had set his sights on a carp of this size as a first stage in his ambition eventually to catch a 'twenty'. He knew that a carp of twenty pounds or more was a magical fish, a catch which few carp anglers ever achieved. He would, though—he knew it! Fortunately, he was a level-headed youngster, and his chief adviser, the bailiff, had persuaded him that any carp was a fine fish, and that time spent in learning to tempt, hook, and land the smaller specimens could never be wasted when at last he caught a big one.

Although the carp spawn had been buried too deeply in the weed for him to observe the actual process of hatching, he had been able to see the tiny fish once they started to move around. He felt a proprietary interest in the carp fry, having been present at their conception, and it was for this reason that he had defended Cypry so stoutly to the boys. The size of this fish puzzled him, though. He thought if it was from this year's hatch—that fish was growing very fast. It was far bigger than any others he had seen. Andy made up his mind to observe this particular carp closely which was not too difficult a task in view of its size. He knew that fish continue to inhabit the area where they had been born at least for some time, which should make things easier. The boy went slowly back to his solitary fishing, still hopeful of catching a double before winter came.

Meanwhile Cypry, hurt and shaken and ignoring the other members of his shoal who swam inquiringly around him as soon as he reappeared, had swum into a quiet recess formed by the branches and trunk of a waterlogged tree which had been blown into the lake during a winter gale three years ago. Here he hung, quivering, only the flutter of the paired pectoral fins betraying his anxiety, while he sought to recover from his terrifying adventure.

Most fish have a favourite holt, or lie, a quiet retreat which they pre-empt as their own, to be used when tired or frightened, a substitute for a home to a creature which has none. This was Cypry's. The tree had taken up a position pointing into the deeper water, its bare, truncated branches like the greyish white bones of some great prehistoric monster. The limbs below the trunk supported it some three feet from the bottom, and projected on either side to form a cage eight feet in length, its roof the tree trunk, its sloping walls the branches, and its floor the lake bed. There were spaces between the branch-walls wide enough to admit even a large fish; once inside, Cypry felt secure. Few anglers fished near, and those who were foolish enough to do so soon lost their tackle when the hooks caught in the still hard wood. Smaller fish were chased away, the older carp ignored him, and the hunting pike seemed to avoid the place. Some of the branches poked gaunt, gesticulating fingers into the air, where they were the favoured perches of kingfishers, robins, and little brown restless wrens.

Every season the club Secretary suggested a working party to remove the tree, but each time Bert dissuaded him. The bailiff knew that it was a good holding place for carp, which need shade and shelter in the summer months. So the once-proud oak remained more still in the water than it had ever been when it was growing, a blessing to the fish and a curse to the anglers, who lost much terminal tackle to its silent rigidity. Only the true expert knew its worth as a carp attractor, a place where he could always find the fish. Patience taught these few men ways of luring the occasional carp from its shelter, to take a bait, then to be held by the rod from its refuge.

Privately, Andy, who was an imaginative child, called the tree 'the Monster'. One day, that fallen tree would save Cypry's life; now it provided for him a haven where he could regain his equilibrium.

The torn flesh of his mouth felt strange, not painful, his side ached where the hot-blooded burning hands had gripped him so cruelly, and his sense of balance had been slightly disturbed by the impact with the hard water, but the secrecy of his hiding place, combined with the cool, healing sensation of the familiar, caressing waterflow was already soothing him. He lay still for several hours, as if asleep, then hunger impelled him once more to look for food, but carefully. He left the holt quickly, fear forgotten, resuming his old pattern of life immediately, almost as if nothing had happened.

Had Cypry but known, many of the carp fry had already been tugged into space as he had, some a number of times. Most forgot completely after a few hours, but a few like the shoal leader, retained within their brains a faint memory which caused them to avoid maggots for a very long time, and to be careful about any unusual objects in the water.

Winter came. The first frosts sent the water temperature plummeting. Icy gales penetrated the wave-ridden shallows, driving the carp to deeper water where the heat remained for a longer period. Weed jungles died, water level rose to cover the lower slopes of the banks, and the drumming vibration of heavy rains sent the young carp accelerating to shelter under sunken logs and branches. The last reluctant leaves fell into the water and were engulfed as if they had never existed, while animal activity in the wood decreased with the year's death.

The little carp fed on.

In the first year of life, carp ignore the winter, eating throughout the cold weather as if their lives depend on doing so, which they do, in a sense. Food is harder to find, so they learn to root among the mud and decaying vegetation of the lake floor, thus establishing a true feeding pattern which will last them their lives.

On through the long freezing January nights, under ice and snow, ignoring gales, accustomed now to rain, the carp continued to feed.

Spring came, birds sang, growing weed appeared once more, creatures multiplied in the water, and food became easier to find. And the carp grew.

By the end of his second summer, at fifteen months old, Cypry was fifteen inches in length, and over five pounds in weight. Fryhood was over; maturity had begun.

4 Maturity

Len Gurel 1985.

Although Cypry had gained nearly five pounds in weight during the first fourteen months of his life, he would not continue to grow at this speed. The average growth rate for carp in Britain is about one pound per year. In a few exceptional waters, such as Cypry's home lake, a few exceptional fish may grow at a rate of three or four pounds a year. All will put on more than average in the first twelve months, and the rate of growth will level later. This is because winter is ignored in the initial year, regular feeding continuing unchecked throughout the cold wet weather.

Cypry's second winter was very different from his first, although not as different as inaccurate books on fish biology and fishing would have us believe. These books often state that carp hibernate or become torpid in the winter, repeating verbatim without bothering about direct observation the information which the writers have culled from other inaccurate books on the same subject.

Specialist carp anglers, many of whom now spend much of their winter fishing time studying carp by watching them in clear waters with polaroid spectacles which cut out some of the light enabling the fish to be seen more easily, know that this is not so. The general pattern in most lakes is that reduction in activity or possibly even a very temporary period of semi-dormancy occurs after the first rapid drop in water temperature, but that as soon as the carp are acclimatized to the colder water, they begin to move around again, and even to feed at times, although with less profit than in the summer months.

Climb a tree near a carp water, and the great fish can be seen, even under ice, constantly circling in a selected area, usually in quite deep water. The intrepid carp angler, cocooned against the cold, continues to fish for his quarry until the season sorrowfully comes to an end in mid-March. The present unofficial winter carp record is a fish of over 35 lbs., while monsters up to this size are frequently caught by these fanatics, even when snow is on the ground and long fingers of brittle ice reach out towards the lake centre from the first-frozen margins.

In the third week of October in Cypry's second year, the frosts came. Just after dark the cloud cover cleared, a huge yellow moon became reflected in the still dark water, and the temperature suddenly fell to several degrees below freezing. Next morning, the bankside animals shivered among stiff speckled white blades of frozen grass, each facet of the frost gems reflecting the climbing sun like a multiplicity of miniscule mirrors. The tracks of birds and animals appeared greener as their feet shook the powdery hoar-frost from everything they touched, and a colony of dormice in the meadow beyond the wood felt strangely dull as their heart-beats slowed in preparation for their long hibernation.

As water cools more slowly than air, it was not until the second morning after the frosts arrived that the carps' complicated nervous system gave warning of the lowered water temperature. The mature fish began to feel less active, their movements slowed, the endless search for nourishment seemed to be too much effort and they began to move into deeper water, where it was still a degree or two warmer. Swimming nervously, fish scented change, which they disliked. The cold weather continued, ice crept imperceptibly out from the edges of the lake as if to absorb each drop of water bit by bit, and at last the carp became almost still, lying torpid at the bottom. Cypry, reluctant, was among them, still with most of his shoal. At this time, the carp would have made little resistance if a net had lifted them from the water, but this comatose state lasted only a few days, while the native British fish—roach, bream, perch, and pike—swam curiously near the carp where they lay like damaged submarines on the lake bed.

By the time the water temperature had been steady at forty-one degrees Fahrenheit for a week and a depression from the Atlantic had chased away the frost bringing gales and rain in their place, Cypry was on the move again. Accustomed now to the colder water, he swam slowly under the bankside trees accompanied by his followers, moving within a thirty to forty yard area in a figure-of-eight pattern, thus defining the region where they would spend most of the remainder of the winter, patrolling ceaselessly, feeding spasmodically, until the spring sun warmed the water and speeded their blood once more. During this period, for the first time Cypry gained no weight, the profit from what feeding he did being directed solely into the energy used by his reduced movements.

Andy watched him whenever he could get to the lake, the only place where he was happy. The boy had discovered that by climbing a tree which he named 'the look-out', he could appreciably increase his field of vision, so that by using his polaroid glasses he could see Cypry's shoal, along with many other fish, whenever the surface was not too disturbed by blustery winter winds. The leader's size made him easy to distinguish although at times Andy confused him with older carp of a similar appearance paying visits from other parts of the pool.

In the early part of next season an incident was to occur that would make Cypry recognizable for ever.

Andy was fifteen now, with less time to spare as he was working fairly disinterestedly for his 'O' level GCE examination at the Comprehensive School in the nearby market town. His parents were practical people with no interest in, or understanding of, the boy's preoccupation with Nature in general and carp in particular. His father was a self-employed master carpenter, a skilled tradesman who soon became irritated by his only child's dreaminess; he wanted his boy to 'get on', so he and his wife gave Andy no encouragement in his spare-time pursuits unless they seemed likely to be in some way helpful towards a future career. Indeed, the carpenter who rarely fished, found himself bitterly regretting having taken his son on the fishing trip which triggered off his obsession.

Unfortunately, the boy was utterly unpractical and disinterested, in his parents' view, his only talents being directed towards his useless interests. His teachers had told them that Andy was intelligent and imaginative with a feeling for and a facility in the use of English, which should stand him in good stead, etc., etc. The parents, stolid and worthy as they were, could see little value in this, as the only written work he seemed to take any trouble over was verse, essays, and a diary concerning fish and animals, whilst in other subjects he was near the bottom of his class, so they nagged him constantly to 'do something useful'. As a result, he became more introspective than ever, growing up to realize that some freak of genetics had made him as different from his parents as if he were not their son. He could discuss nothing with them; there was no point of contact. They often complained of neighbours' children who hung around the streets of the town getting into mischief, yet in their opinion their own boy was as bad in another way.

Even when this winter Andy wrote a poem for which he was highly praised by the English master, which was published in the school magazine and actually mentioned in the local paper, his parents were not proud of him, as others would have been, he thought resentfully.

The poem, which was remarkably mature, was called *Animals in Winter*:

> Food-drunk, sleep-drunk,
> In the frosty glen,
> Dreams the burly badger
> Hidden from all men.
>
> Curled small, like a ball,
> Down a lonely hole,
> Dors the tiny dormouse
> Dreaming he's a mole.

Just asleep, a squirrel sleek,
High up in his tree,
Wakes on warmer nights, and walks
Through woods, uneasily.

Fox creeps, never sleeps,
Quietly through the farm;
Winter doesn't worry him—
There's chicken in the barn.

Peripatetic, extra-frenetic,
Cold birds search the ground;
Hard-glazed eyes in perpetual motion,
Survival, but no sound.

Fish still swim, in the dim
Colder winter water;
Wrapped securely in their slime
They lie in the tilting thermocline.

Weasels whicker, stoats snore,
Rabbits quiver, rats gnaw;
A multiplicity of hearts
Beat slower in the winter.

Incapable of making things with his hands, his latent creativity had produced this poem after a lesson at school on Nature poetry. When he tentatively took the magazine home to his parents, open at his piece, eagerly hoping for some unaccustomed praise, his spirit shrank as his father, with a contemptuous expression on his coarse red face, glanced at the verses then flung the magazine to the floor, saying hurtfully:

'Think you're another .... Shakespeare, do you? Your mother and I'd think much more of you if you showed us something *useful* for once, such as a good report, or 'igh marks in Maths or Science, instead of that ... that muck!'

Andy's eyes filled with tears at this curt dismissal of his innermost thoughts, revealed on paper for the first time. He wandered slowly down to his beloved lake, feeling crushed.

Why, his father hadn't even read it! Why didn't they understand? Why must he be the same as them? Of course he wasn't
going to be a poet, nor a carpenter, either, he thought bitterly.
He didn't know what he wanted to do. He sat down sadly on
a cold tree stump, confused thoughts dwelling on the seemingly
unbridgeable gap between the generations, but soon he saw a
carp moving, and he forgot his troubles in joy at the sight of
the living creature.

Later his mother found the discarded poem and read it
through twice, stumbling over the unfamiliar words, some of
which meant nothing to her. She thought it was quite good,
really, and meant to speak to the boy about it. She never
did, though; after all, she had a lot to do.

For Cypry, winter water was empty water. Everywhere he
looked, there was emptiness and blankness. Weeds were dead,
water lilies shrunken, trees leafless, creatures few. A harsh,
hard brightness filled the lake during the few short hours of
light in clear weather; for the rest of the time, while towering
cumulus clouds rolled overhead, the fishes' world was dull and
dreary. Long lonely nights added to the gloom; the icy water
underlined it. The carp felt drained of energy, unanimated.
There was no fear now, only boredom. Cypry swam his
beat mechanically, without interest, as if some life-force within
him had died with the summer. He did not know that the cold
water had caused changes in his body, slowing his heart-beats
to reduce the level of activity, allowing him to function on the
little food available. The life-force had not died, but was merely
suspended, awaiting only warmth to re-animate it. So the carp
passed the hated winter till suns of spring re-visited the lake,
reviving semi-dormant life in fish, plant, and the myriad
creatures of the water, to quicken the carp to a passionate new
awareness of their surroundings.

In May and June, depending on the weather, there is a
population explosion in fertile lakes, as in a country when
its soldiers return from a war. Water plants grow almost
visibly, their dependent insects and animals multiplying with
incredible rapidity, until a bucket of water drawn from the
pool is thick with millions of organisms. It is at this time that
the carp start to feed seriously, tails waving high above their
heads, sometimes breaking the surface as the fish suck in huge

quantities of mud, from which they extract their food. Rolling curtains of fine mud specks stain the water, betraying the carp's presence beneath—'smokescreening' carp anglers call it. These few weeks of concentrated gorging enabled Cypry to increase his winter weight by two pounds, almost double the total amount he would gain during the whole of the rest of the year.

Strangely, this mass feeding phenomenon seems to cease just as the fishing starts in mid-June, to the lasting fury of frustrated anglers who have watched the unattainable with longing during the three months when they are prevented by law from attempting to catch the protected fish. Cypry himself was temporarily sated before the anglers descended upon the lake again. He felt a different fish now that the water was warm. He was full of power and well-being, confident and unafraid, big enough to ignore the hungriest hunting pike, strong enough to escape any danger which might present itself. His belly felt curiously full and tight, not only from good eating, but with the milt which his glands had been secretly producing for some time, ready for him to take his part in the mystery of spawning. This euphoria culminated in early June with his first participation in the brief, ecstatic honeymoon of the fishes, then, after a rest period, he returned to a normal pattern of feeding for a couple of hours each day, at dawn and dusk.

Although carp are primarily bottom feeders, they can learn to take food from the surface, especially in hot weather when their habit of swimming near the top brings floating objects within their range of vision, or scent if it is dark. Crafty anglers take advantage of this apparently unnatural custom by casting bread upon the waters to tempt the fish to feed on it. Three days after the start of the season, very early one still morning while mist-devils were still rising from the water, Cypry was cautiously investigating various floating articles at the edge of a bed of water crowfoot, when he found some of this bread, discovering that it was very tasty. The fifth piece he sucked in, mouth wide, contained a big hook tied to a fine monofilament nylon line wound on to a fixed spool fishing reel which was attached to a powerful carp rod. The rod was held somewhat shakily by Andy, who had almost let it fall to the ground as the floating crust disappeared in a huge exciting swirl. He made no mistake, however. As the fish turned away, the line lying on the water tightened quickly, the boy swept the rod back hard, and the carp was on.

This time, Cypry knew instantly what had happened, and in a blind panic to avoid his previous experience, he contorted his body impelled by the powerful tail to its full speed of over twenty-five miles an hour within a few feet, heading for the middle of the lake. Andy's rod, spring-like, bent to absorb the pull, the clutch chattered as the line was torn off the spool so fast that the transparent nylon was almost invisible. Andy's face was white. Never had he imagined such speed. He had been stalking Cypry for some time, so he was almost sure it was the shoal leader he had hooked, and he knew anyway that he was into a good fish.

For twenty, thirty, forty yards the carp ran against the vibrating tug at his mouth, then his strength began to fail, his speed to slacken. Immediately he slowed, Andy began to recover line, coping easily with occasional short rushes, until his fish was only a few yards out, boring sullenly on a circular course. The boy's mouth felt dry. For several minutes the fight continued, but gradually Cypry was forced to the surface by the pressure of the line against his mouth, and he began to flounder, exhausted and beaten. Gingerly, Andy reached for the big landing net, slid it into the water, towing the tired fish over the opening in the net. As he lifted, the metal arm of the net touched Cypry's side almost exactly as he saw his enemy for the first time, vision distorted by the moving water over his eye. The dual shock galvanized him into a last despairing run. Kiting sideways, he shot away from the net, taking the angler by surprise, his momentum carrying him crashing into some underwater branches ten yards away. He felt a pain in his side as a sharp piece of wood pierced it, then he was hauled out into the open water once more. Andy, recovering quickly, though with a sickening certainty that the fish was lost, had correctly dropped his rod point, applying immediate sidestrain before the carp could entangle the line among the snags. This time, there was no mistake at the net.

Cypry was caught again.

Gently, almost reverently, Andy placed the heavy net containing the supine fish on the grass, wetted his hands, and began to remove the hook, which was firmly set in the side of the mouth. Realizing that extraction by the usual method would cause the barb to hurt the fish, Andy cut the line near the hook, then pulled the bend from outside the mouth until the eye of the hook emerged from the flesh and it was out. This prevented the flesh from being torn by pulling against the needle-sharp barb. Hurriedly the boy detached the landing net handle, weighing the net section on his spring balance, while Cypry gave a few ineffectual flaps of his tail in protest. With the weight of the net subtracted the fish weighed just over eight pounds. His biggest carp! Andy's hands still trembled. You beautiful thing, he thought. Then he looked round proudly, hoping he had been seen landing the fish. To his delight, two older anglers had strolled up to see how big it was.

'Good carp,' remarked one. 'Great fight, too. You handled it well.'

Andy glowed. By the lake, he was someone; fishing was something he could do, and be successful at, too. Better still, the man who had spoken, whom Andy recognized as a well known local carp angler, noticing the palpable air of excitement and achievement which surrounded the boy, got out his camera and took two quick pictures of the carp and its captor.

'Bring you the prints next time I'm out,' he said, smiling at Andy's obvious pleasure.

Then the happy boy picked up his fish, lowering it into the water. Cypry gave a deep breath, and the gasping, choking feeling was relieved at once. He had been out of the life-giving water for no more than four minutes, not long enough to do him any harm physically, especially as he had been treated carefully, but long enough to be unpleasant. As he flicked his broad tail to swim slowly away from the supporting hands, Andy noticed for the first time the small injury inflicted by the branch whilst the fish was being played. A few scales had been removed, a little red flesh showed. Next time he saw Cypry, the place had healed into a white scar, about three-quarters of an inch in length, high on the left side close to the root of the dorsal fin; it was by this mark that he was always able to identify 'his' carp in the future.

The hole in the mouth, which was little more than a pin-prick, thanks to the humane way in which the hook had been extracted, stopped aching almost at once, and Cypry was feeding again within a few hours. But once more he had learnt.

His brain retained an impression, undefined but definite, of danger connected with wriggling white maggots, floating bread, the long irritating line he had seen leading from his mouth, and the blurred figures on the bank. He was now conditioned to regard people as enemies and some foods as connected inexplicably with them, and so to be avoided. From this time on, he fed with circumspection, inspecting and rejecting many large and unnatural-looking offerings cast into the water by hopeful anglers.

Cypry also found that he could see the moving shapes amid that stifling element by day and even on bright nights. His sight was excellent, though his sense of smell and the sensitivity of those protractile lips and fleshy barbules was more important to him for feeding purposes. Whenever a bankside movement caught his eye, he fled the area rapidly; whenever an edible object seemed in some way suspicious—and often he was actually able to see the line growing out from the bait—he left it alone. So the two-year-old carp was beginning to show that legendary caution which has led writers of the past to conclude that they were almost uncatchable : —

> *Of all the fish that swim the watery mead*
> *Not one in cunning can the carp exceed.*

says a writer of many years ago.

It is a scientific fact that the carp's brain is, in proportion, the largest of any fresh-water fish; that it is capable of learning has been proved many times. This capacity even transcends, in the opinion of many experienced carp anglers, the simple conditioned reflex of which many animals are capable. Whether the carp can think, reason or communicate as some assert, remains doubtful, although who is to say with certainty that they cannot?

Having lived for two years, spawned, been caught twice, acted as shoal leader and learnt to come to terms with some of the problems and dangers of his environment, Cypry was ready for the next stage of his life; the semi-solitary existence of the big mature carp.

5 'Double'

Ian Gwel 1985

Winter monotony succeeded summer pleasure in Cypry's third year as inevitably as season followed season. The life cycle of the animals, birds, and insects which revolved around the stretch of water was repeated with general similarity, but specific differences, once more.

Weather and old age caused most of the change.

The old heron, defeated ultimately by its only enemy, apart from man, died at last in an autumn storm by the side of the lake it knew so well; Bert the bailiff found two evil-looking carrion crows tearing at the carcase next morning. The eyes were already gone and the body was covered with ants and beetles. He was succeeded by two of his children, to whom he had bequeathed the riches of the water by showing them how to fish it some years ago.

A big dog fox, its earth unfairly blocked, was hunted down in the wood after a long exhausting chase from a farm three miles away, where it had been watching some busy chicken-runs from a covert in preparation for a night raid.

Gales brought down numerous branches, some crashing into

the water, sending fish sliddering violently away from the huge splashes, the vibrations from which shocked their nervous systems.

A rare Christmas ammil encased every twig and blade of grass in an uneven translucent shaft of ice, petrifying all motion as if to preserve each plant and branch and bramble for ever. Before the quick thaw, the sun struck multi-coloured light from reflecting prismatic surfaces, until the smooth ice became dripping water, and the unfrozen vegetation was released, to move gently to the breeze once more.

Cypry emerged from the deeps one morning to find a strange hard light reflected in the still water from a heavy snowfall which had transformed overnight every surface in the wood beyond. The images of the whitened tree boles contrasted oddly with the black water, a pied and curious scene which frightened the fish by its unfamiliarity, so that he slid back into the safe depths in confusion. A kingfisher cried sharply as it flashed overhead, seeking a snowless branch on which to rest, while chaffinches and yellowhammers sang their dismay to each other: they knew food was scarce, when snow was down.

Winter hung on until May that year; the water was still grim-cold on Cypry's third birthday. Carp spawned late that summer and the soaring swallows wished they had never returned as they swooped low over the water, searching for their insect food, of which there was a dearth this year. Often the darting birds had to be content with a quick, splashy drink, scaring the fish below, which mistook them for their enemy, the kingfisher.

On the seventh of July the weather changed with the suddenness which characterizes the uncertain climate in Britain. A hot southerly wind blew across Europe from the Mediterranean, the temperature rose by some twenty degrees overnight, and a belated summer had come to Cartench. Day after blazing day the sun poured out heat from a cloudless sky, the temperature of the water increased with unusual rapidity, and the warmth-loving carp were content.

Perhaps it was the longed-for return to revitalizing conditions, perhaps it was coincidence, but it was at this time that Cypry left the shoal.

He was now a double-figure fish, the carp-man's 'double' of over ten pounds in weight; not large for a king carp, but already at a greater weight than most British fresh-water fish would ever attain, however long they lived. Bigger carp tend to be more solitary, although at times they will bask, swim, or feed with a few chosen companions. Like the anglers who fish solely for them, carp are independent, individualistic, unpredictable in behaviour, yet at times curiously creatures of habit. Cypry felt an urge to know more of his universe, to explore the acres of liquidity beyond the small corner in which he had lived up to the present. If he was to be the complete master of his world, he must be familiar with every variation in the configuration of the lake bed; he must have knowledge of each hole and sunken tree; every aspect of the water must be closely investigated, for necessity might render the knowledge invaluable in times of danger.

This instinct to explore may well be a distant racial memory, for the Asian carp was a much-travelled river fish, not bound by the confines of an enclosed lake.

There was much to see even here. The pool was old, natural, and large. Many thousands of years ago, in a remote period of geological time, a shallow depression had been scooped in the ancient land by the action of many sharp-edged boulders carried by a retreating glacier. As the ice rolled away from the land, rains had come, springs had appeared, a stream had formed and gradually the hollow filled, water being unable to escape through the semi-impervious rock.

Spring- and stream-fed, the lake found its own level and boundaries which left it crescent-shaped, some thirteen acres in extent. Two small protuberances became islands. Unicellular life began to appear in the water, plants and their seeds brought down by the stream, rooted and grew; the lake became fertile. Creatures of the water spread, multiplied, fed on each other.

Later came the fish. Brought, perhaps, on the feet of birds as tiny eggs at first from other established waters, then introduced by man, the native pike, perch, and bream found conditions to their liking and spread rapidly. After many years tench and the stranger carp were put in, to grow and be caught for food. Bushes and trees grew on the banks, hemming the lake in, except for one open patch of green where the track, once an ancient roadway, ran. Oaks, elms, and chestnuts spread, forming a belt of woodland which effectively isolated the pool, apart from to those who followed the track.

The lake had seen much of the pageantry of the country's history.

Primitive peoples of the past, skin-clad and brutish, had drunk its clear waters; early farmers had supplemented their inadequate food supplies by catching and eating the tasty fish; Celtic priests had known its secrets. Roman legionaries, far from home, dusty and tired after a forced march to put down a revolt among the Dumnonii had rested briefly on its banks, wondering at the peace of the place, until cursing centurions word-lashed them to their feet, to continue a duty which would end only in death or disgust.

Norman barons, exploring their expropriated country, reined in their steaming horses beside the lake, casting covetous eyes on it and the surrounding land, imagining themselves granted the demesne by King William, building a castle on the hill nearby, then defending their new baronry against all-comers with their private army of followers.

But it was the Church which won it in the end, as so often in those priest-dominated times, when the Abbot of the Benedictine Order of Lisieux was given the land by Henry the First in the year 1123.

The monastery took eleven years to finish, and was built on a knoll near the north end of the lake, with the feeder stream after it left the pool flowing through its lower grounds, to provide drinking water, washing, and some measure of sanitation. This was the lake's busiest period so far. Black-habited monks, cheerful and hard-working, cleared paths round the water for access, after processing from the monastery each day, led by the Abbot and intoning the customary Latin prayer asking blessing on their manual work, and the deep-toned angelus sounded through the woods. For the first time the lake was fished seriously, to provide the food for Friday meals; as it was their stew-pond, the monks kept it heavily overstocked to make the catching of fish almost a routine matter. Two hundred years of benevolent monkish ownership passed before the carp were introduced, long wild commons from abbey ponds in France, prolific and nourishing to eat. The wild carp increased rapidly; soon there were thousands present, rarely over four pounds in weight, but satisfyingly easy to catch.

At the Dissolution of the Monasteries, the land was transferred to an ancestor of the Wyatt-Smythes for 'services to the King'. This ancestor had been a notorious Cornish wrecker, who lured ships on to the cruel rocks by lighting false beacons, then presented half his loot to the king, who, greedy for wealth, ignored its source and even honoured the evil donor.

From the Middle Ages onwards, the lake saw fewer people. Some of the lord's peasants were given permission to fish it for food, their wives washed clothes in the water, and an occasional poacher, desperate to escape from the reeve's dogs on his trail, swam to one of the islands, to hide, trembling among the thick undergrowth until the danger was past, but for most of the year, the fish lived and bred undisturbed.

The eighteenth century saw walks, rustic bridges and gazebos built around the property in the fashion of the time. Picnics and parties took place amongst the trees, perfumed beaus arranged secret assignations with ladies, whose skirts brushed the grasses, in the summer houses by the lake, and boating became popular in summer.

The Victorians kept the place tidy but showed little interest in rustic pursuits; remains of the rotted bridges and other buildings were still there, but the place became neglected and overgrown during this century, while a succession of Wyatt-Smythes helped build the Empire and fought endless bloody wars in far-off lands, until just after the Second World War, when the local fishing club got the lease at last. Now it was well-cared for; beautiful. The anglers who fished there were much envied throughout the angling world, and it was often referred to as a 'typical English lake'.

The legacy of its long history was an indescribable atmosphere of dignity and tradition which grew on those who spent much time there, and the great rolling king carp added to this atmosphere, although only the more perceptive were aware of this feeling. To the rest, it was just a pleasant spot to fish.

To Cypry, it was a world without end.

Unaware, uncaring of the long past as he slid slowly onwards beside the yellow flowering water lilies on his journey of investigation, he was concerned only with those aspects of the life of the lake which affected him. Feeding and the avoidance of danger were the main motivations of his existence, but of intimations of pleasure he was capable. He experienced them now, as he left his familiar patrolling grounds for the first time. Light was strong, water warm, food everywhere, he was of the species kings of freshwater, so what could life hold for him but satisfaction, if not ecstasy? Keenly alive to the flow of the lucent water past his powerful body, alert to each new sight and sound in or near the water-world around him, ever expectant of peril and ready with an instantaneous reaction to it, the carp swam on into the unknown.

Three members of the shoal, more adventurous than their companions, followed Cypry for a while, but gradually their movements became less decisive. They were diverted to examine various feeding prospects, by which time Cypry was lost to them, and they turned back. Their time for individuality had not yet come. On their return, the biggest, an unusually deep-bellied leather carp without scales and thick-skinned, became leader in Cypry's place.

Swimming south, Cypry noticed little of interest to begin with, until the water lilies fell away, revealing a wide bay, into which he swam. As he did so, he rose to the surface, long dorsal and back emerging into the air. The sun struck hot upon his scales, and enjoying the feeling the carp continued to swim lazily in this manner, as others were already doing over the lake.

Almost immediately, there was a splash behind him. Slightly alarmed, he sounded, then levelled turning to see what had caused the vibration which had startled him. Seeing something floating, he angled upwards until he was again partly out of the water, approaching the object cautiously, foot by foot, like a ship coming into dock, until his working mouth was only a few inches away. It was a piece of floating crust. Cypry could see the line coming from it, lying along the water. Contemptuously, he submerged, allowing the crust to pass close over him, not realizing that he was almost causing a novice carp angler fifteen yards away behind a tree to have heart failure at the sight of his bait, as he thought, so nearly taken.

Turning right, the former shoal leader followed the floating line, curious to find out where it led. Soon he was able to recognize the water-distorted shapes of the anglers, several of them, in an open, grassy area, clear of trees, where the track came down from the village. Andy, who had names for all the swims and pitches, called this 'the beach' because of the stony, sloping bank between the grass and the water. It was attractive to anglers, being easy to cast from. As Cypry surfaced again, one of the men pointed and a number of pieces of bread were launched in his direction, flying heavily through the air like Alice's bread and butter flies. Cypry ignored them, swimming arrogantly across in front of the beach within full view of the frustrated anglers, as if deliberately defying them. Unless he ate one of the baits, they could do him no harm, as he knew quite well by now.

For some time the carp continued to swim aimlessly in this manner as if the anglers' baits did not exist, then as the afternoon heat became greater, he moved into the shadow of the water lilies on the far side of the bay, where he rested, his back just touching the floating green lily plates, causing them to shiver lightly from time to time. There were many other carp among the water lily carpet, lying stationary, absorbing the heat of the surface water while using the protection of the disc-like leaves against the direct rays of the burning sun. Each fish was aware of, yet indifferent to, the presence of others, concentrating solely on the pleasurable sensations induced by the all too rare heat wave conditions, while breathing the extra oxygen created by the water plants. Each was a sensuous entity, possessed through its tactile water-contact by the stimulation of the warmed element in which it existed.

The sweating, shirtless anglers knew that the carp were there, but they were also aware that the fish were not feeding. All comparatively inexperienced in fishing, they were convinced that even if a fish was to be hooked, the tough weed stalks would break their lines, so they went on fruitlessly fishing the now empty open water, noisily cursing the excessive heat, telling each other that the best carp angler alive could not catch fish in this weather.

Later, another figure, hard to distinguish against the background of trees in his dark green and brown clothes, appeared opposite the lily bed, some twenty yards from the others. This man sat unmoving for nearly half an hour watching the weed closely, occasionally using binoculars for this purpose. He was a carp specialist, an expert angler whom long experience had taught exactly how to catch carp in the prevailing conditions; he would have one on within the hour. Not realizing this, the unsuccessful anglers laughed at him as he patiently scanned the water.

Movements slow and deliberate in the oppressive heat, the expert exchanged the spool on his reel for one containing a heavier line of fifteen pounds breaking strain, putting a small piece of crust on the large hook. With one last look through the binoculars to ensure that he had pin-pointed the 'blunt end' of one particular fish, the man got carefully to his feet, released the pick-up of the reel, and swung the crust from the rod tip, letting go of the line at precisely the correct moment. The bait flew through the air in a shallow curve, landing unerringly on the water lily leaf chosen by the angler, causing too small a vibration to disturb the basking carp. With great concentration, the carp specialist raised the tubular fibre glass rod, tightening the line until the crust eased fractionally along the leaf to its edge, then tipped almost imperceptibly into the water. Unaware of anything but the white bait, knowing that if it had been correctly placed only a few inches from the carp's mouth a fish would be unable to resist sucking it in eventually, possibly immediately, even though it was not genuinely interested in feeding, the angler, still holding his ten-foot rod, watched the line intently where it lay across the leaves.

The crust had appeared suddenly, but not frighteningly, five inches from Cypry's slowly water-gulping mouth, with no appreciable water movement to cause alarm. One moment it was not there, the next it was as if it had always been, rocking naturally at the suck of water into his mouth. At first Cypry ignored the thing, but he could taste and smell it as food and it loomed so large in his eye after ten minutes, so tempting, that he contorted his body a little, then extended the protractile lips, beginning to draw the bait towards him like a slow-motion vacuum cleaner. The fish felt safe among the weed; he could not reason sufficiently to connect a piece of bread seen here with a similar appearance in open water. Carp which have learnt that floating baits are dangerous under normal

circumstances will often take unhesitatingly if they are presented in weed, and this Cypry was about to do.

Seeing the slight movements of leaf and bait, the angler
knew that he was about to have a take. He readied himself
motionless on the bank, rod held low, an extension of his
arm. With the bait no more than two inches from Cypry's open
mouth, a long sudden form flashed by Cypry's head, causing
him to turn in panic, and the crust disappeared in an enormous
boil of water. The line shot off the leaves, the angler struck
hard, the tail of a hooked fish thrashed the surface and the
resulting commotion made every fish in the area accelerate
away leaving the whole bed of lilies rocking with waves from
the displaced water as if an underwater explosion had occurred.

The fish which had taken the bait Cypry had been about to
swallow was a long, thin, fully-scaled carp, little more than
Cypry's weight, but over a foot longer. This was a wild carp,
or wildie, direct descendant of the fish introduced by the
monks so long ago. Its regularly-placed bronze scales, streamlined shape and small head made it seem a different species
beside the thick stomach and huge, irregular scaling of the king
mirrors, such as Cypry, which were now the dominant variety
in the lake.

There were few of these wildies left. Realizing that they
bred too rapidly, producing too many small fish, the club had
netted most of them out, transferring them to a nearby barren
canal, recently recovered from an industrial pollution which
had wiped out the native fish stock. Here they gave great
sport to the city anglers who fished among the assorted débris
of the suburban canal arm, while the few remaining wild commons interbred with the king carp, thus increasing their own
growth rate. This mixture of strains meant that these fish
were not now genuine wild carp, but they still retained most
of the characteristics of the original stock.

One of these was speed and power. No fish fights for its
freedom like a wildie. A salmon of the same weight, hooked
in still water with no current to aid it and on the same tackle,
would have surrendered in half the time of the carp that saved
Cypry from being caught yet again.

First, the hooked fish dived frantically into the lilies hoping
to entangle the infuriating line, but the angler lifted the rod

high, pulling the frightened fish to the surface where it thrashed furiously amongst the lily leaves, clearing a space for itself in its frenzy. Unable to progress further the wildie shot off in the opposite direction, charging blindly through the swaying green stems until it emerged into the open, leaving behind it circular leaves which floated to the top of the water like miniature rafts, their stalks cleanly severed by the fast travelling nylon monofilament line. The angler lowered his rod as the fish ran, thankfully relaxing the pressure as it tore out into the lake. Feeling this, the carp swam faster, not realizing that it was doing exactly as its captor intended. Well away from weed and snags, the carp would be allowed to swim until it tired, then brought to the net.

Cypry, upset by the noise, had sunk into deeper water, where his increased angle of vision made it possible for him to watch the antics of the hooked fish as it streaked overhead, the line leading from its mouth clearly visible. In company with several other big carp, Cypry, possessed by curiosity, followed the gyrations of the hooked wildie from a few yards away, running when it ran and turning with it, as if towed behind. At last the exhausted fish was brought in by that irresistible force against its mouth, where it swam in decreasing circles until it was netted almost ten minutes from the time it had taken the bait. The free carp followed it almost to the net, sheering off at the last moment as the struggling wildie was lifted from the water to its hell. The expert saw the other fish, but remained unsurprised. It was not the first time he had observed this habit. He was very pleased with his catch; a wild carp of nearly twelve pounds was indeed an exceptional fish. They rarely grow bigger.

The less experienced anglers, who had been watching the spectacular fight with some envy, gathered round to see the fish with murmurs of admiration. The expert allowed them to pick his brains about the method of hot weather fishing. He was a tolerant man, prepared to help others, although sure he was wasting his time on this occasion. As he walked away to seek a quieter spot where he could continue to stalk individual fish undisturbed, he saw pieces of bread being cast haphazardly into the lilies, and smiled to himself. Two hours later, only one of the anglers had hooked a fish, which broke him immediately because he had not felt it worth the trouble to change to a heavier line, as advised by the expert. By evening, the carp catcher, who had caught two more fish, was able to see from his latest pitch across the lake that all the other anglers had returned to their useless open water fishing as he had expected, saying no doubt that his fish from the lilies was 'just luck'. They never learn, he reflected, which is why they will remain unsuccessful anglers all their lives. Then he forgot them in the joy of the chase.

Cypry and two of the bigger carp had stayed in the vicinity long enough to see the released wildie returned to the water, shaking its head. All had been caught themselves, so they knew what the fish felt. What they had seen today would help to make them more cautious of their own feeding in the future. Cypry spent the rest of the evening, until the flaming ball of the descending sun disappeared below the tree line, cruising along the edge of the weed on the south side of the beach, out of reach of the anglers.

Night came. The darkening water cooled slowly, fish became more active. Sleepy day birds sang their evening songs before retiring and bank voles plopped busily in and out of the water, submerging at the slightest sound. Tiny pipistrelle bats, ugly but incredibly quick, snaked their sound-controlled flights under the trees, twisting and turning to catch the last insects as they dropped despairing with the sun into the black water. A big white barn owl, originator of many country ghost stories of the past, flew noiselessly up the track ready to pounce on the first scratchy mouse movement selected by his huge ears, while hundreds of light years away innumerable brilliant stars decorated the night sky. The air was still, the wood almost silent, peace broken only by the occasional hum and arced headlights of a car on the distant road. Across the lake, a dark figure flitted from tree to tree—the bailiff, alone now, checking for poachers, the only human shape in a microcosmic animal and vegetable world, adapted to move inconspicuously in it by long years of careful practice.

Few people see the night. To most, it is but a passing inconvenience, a suspension of faculties long lost, an hiatus in time, to be passed in rapid sleep till new light restored vision and confidence. Darkness induces an elemental fear, fed by transmitted time-memories of snuffling hunting beasts and imagined horrific spirits whose horrid unreality haunts lonely unlit countryside with evil intent. Reality is otherwise. Night can be learned, for those who care to do so. Bailiffs and game-keepers, night anglers and naturalists study to enjoy the quiet dark hours, knowing that man has nothing to fear in them but other men. To the initiated, each identifiable rustle and squeak in the undergrowth is but evidence of the pullulating animal life which increases at nightfall, not the insubstantial footsteps of some long-dead monkish phantom. The whisper of wings and the sudden splash of a joy-leaping carp punctuate the long hours of obscurity to the reclining angler, relaxed as never by day, petty troubles forgotten in a new awareness of a night-awoken life beyond his own.

6 Journey

Len Gurd 1985

Normally, to Cypry, night was but an extension of day, with little alteration in the pattern of his movements. Keen vision largely useless except in moonlight, he relied on his other highly developed senses; those of smell, taste, and touch. Shock waves travelling through the water like radio waves through the air warned his central nervous system of the nearness of other objects, enabling him to swim safely at full speed as easily as in daylight, while he could smell food from afar.

This night was different, though, as it was the first of his journey and he was in unfamiliar waters. It was still warm at dusk, so he continued to move onwards until the lily pads came to an abrupt end. Beyond was clear water, with something dark overhead, through which patches of the sky appeared. He swam up to investigate, finding that above him was a broken roof of tree branches, some of which, borne down by their own weight, lay under water, forming a helpful curtain through which he could proceed. Before he could do so he heard coming from nearby a number of loud sucking sounds, which carp anglers call, expressively, 'cloops'. Knowing that this usually indicated surface feeding, Cypry pushed his way through the branches, feeling them slide pleasantly along his smooth side, to find out what was going on. Almost at once his mouth came up against a floating object which he identified immediately as a piece of crust. Alarmed, he stopped, then backed away. There was a swirl and a cloop beside him, and by the dim light he was able to see another piece of bread being taken down by a carp larger than himself. Surprised, he lay still, waiting.

All at once the clooping seemed to start up in every direction, almost as if a signal to feed had been given. Everywhere, carp were taking with abandon, sucking down the floating crusts which had been thrown in by anglers before leaving, and which had drifted into the sides of the lake. Still Cypry waited, expecting each minute to feel the water-borne thud of acceleration of a hooked fish. When this did not occur, he became bolder, swimming close to a carp over twice his weight which was confidently taking in crust after crust, having learnt long ago that there were no hooks in these at night, when the anglers had gone. At last, Cypry edged cautiously up to a big sloppy piece of the bread, extending his lips until they could marginally feel its texture. He could detect no hard hook or line, so he swallowed it slowly, pharyngeal teeth grinding at the food as it reached his throat. It tasted good, so abandoning caution, he too sucked and slurped noisily at the bread, feeding avidly until all was gone. The wavelets from each disturbance spread across the dark water, merging and crossing until diminished, they lapped gently at the bank.

Bert the bailiff, trudging silently home up the track after his last nightly circumnavigation of the lake, smiled briefly to himself as he heard the fish feeding. Wouldn't them anglers just like to be down here now, he thought? Some years ago, he and the club Secretary had been given special permission for a night's fishing on the lake, to catch some carp for a visiting biologist to examine, and they'd had a carp every fifteen minutes or so until one in the morning. The fish knew it was safe to feed now. Proper cunning, them carp! The bailiff walked on into the night towards his little cottage, not using the big torch which hung at his belt, as much at home now as during the brightest day. Every night sound was familiar to his trained ear; his slow almost noiseless step disturbed the animals but little. He moved so quietly at night that on the few occasions anglers had attempted to break the rules by fishing the lake more than an hour after sunset, he had been able to put a hand on their shoulders before they suspected his presence, thus frightening them so much that they would never have gone near the place again in the dark, even if Bert had not succeeded in having them expelled from the club.

By the time the bread had all been eaten, night air had slightly cooled the surface layer of the water and Cypry went deeper towards the lake centre. Very soon, he found himself in shallow water once again. Slow swimming brought him up against solid ground, where his watery world ended, and another, harder world began. His back in air, Cypry followed the contours of the bank for some time, puzzled by the amount of turn necessary to keep contact with the place where the water solidified. After an hour of this peregrination, the carp suddenly recognized a projecting rock as one which he had passed several times before; he had been circling an island. He stopped, suspended in the water, then half-rolled on the surface to get his bearings. Stationary again, while the water-roar of his roll travelled off into the night, he could hear the thud of other fish leaping, the occasional harsh shriek of a quarrelling water bird, the distant melancholy call of a lonely owl. Bored, he sank deeper, approaching an end of the island which had smelt of food each time he had passed. Angling downwards, the ever-hungry carp reached the muddy lake bed, tracking down the food scent. When he arrived at the source of the smell, he found that it was an extensive carpet of tiny fresh-water snails, a favourite fish food. Tail up, body at 45 degrees, mouth greedily gulping quantities of snails, to be crunched by the throat teeth, Cypry fed happily for the next hour.

Many other fish were feeding on the snails; Cypry saw dimly, or sensed, members of his own species, mingled with a huge shoal of orange-eyed tench, for which the lake was famous, interspersed with the odd big bream, wide slab-side gleaming dully in the shallow water. These tench were peculiar fish. Dark in colour, less 'intelligent' than the carp, they were strangely hard to catch at times, whilst at others they fed blindly, being caught in great numbers. They were called 'doctor fish' by people of long ago, who spoke of seeing other fish rub against them deliberately. A Roman writer saw tench being applied to the feet of a sick person, the thick coating of mucus on their bodies having curative properties, he was told. They rarely grew larger than eight pounds in weight, but were powerful for their size, although less so than the carp. The smaller bream were stupid fish, unmuscular, the delight of the novice angler, being easy to catch once located. The various species fed amicably side by side; they had nothing to fear from each other, while competition was made unnecessary by the millions of helpless snails waiting to be eaten. The feeding fish were close but never touching; their ceaseless, pig-like rooting produced long strings of silver bubbles which rose in columns to the surface, betraying the existence of the hungry fish beneath.

Within an hour, in the early hours of the morning, Cypry was replete, so he left the feeding ground for deeper water between the island and the mainland, where he lay on the bottom until daylight, as near to sleep as a fish can be, tilted slightly to one side, motionless except for the ever-moving mouth and gills.

The first light from the still-hidden sun irradiated the lake at last, dark began to recede and night-hunting animals slunk tiredly back to their holes full of food, ready for rest. Some which had set out hopefully at sunset never returned, having been caught and eaten by owls, foxes, stoats, weasels, and badgers. Mortality was greatest among the mice and shrews who had many enemies, but a few nervous rabbits had screamed to a terrified end under the needle-point claws of the blood-drinking stoats, while near the mouth of one of the badger tunnels a great grey rat had died fighting when he un-expectedly met the occupant. Preferring to eat the juicy earthworms which were so easy to catch, the badger disliked rats. Pushing the carcase aside, scenting the imminent sunrise, she lumbered down the run through the bushes made by the constant passage of her family to where the three cubs were playing, sliding down an earthy bank, biting and nuzzling each other. Licking the painful rat bites on her muzzle, the female badger shepherded the cubs into the obscurity of the sett; she knew there was danger in daylight.

Thirteen distinct bird species joined in the melodic chorus of approaching day, their intermingled songs blending with the whisper of a westerly wind through the leaves. In the lake, long predatory pike, and their jackals the smaller perch, digested their food after a night of hunting. Between them, they had killed and eaten 632 roach and bream during the past twenty-four hours, thus helping to thin out the many thousands of these over-prolific fish which crowded the water and, if allowed to breed unchecked, would stifle all life but their own. The change-over from nocturnal to diurnal life was less marked in the water than on land. Fish were active for most of the time, although in lakes such as Cartench, where there was no night fishing which meant no bankside interference with shallow water feeding areas, most of the fish population, especially the carp, had learned to feed chiefly at night. Cypry had lain unmoving between two and four a.m., but at first light he was on the move again, prepared for an early morning feed should opportunity present itself, although not committed to an eager search for food immediately. Light intensity had some considerable effect on his movements; it was the increasing amount of light filtering through the upper water layers which activated him now. Instead of continuing his exploration—he was incapable of a pre-determined order of procedure, his journey being spasmodic and haphazard rather than systematic—he returned to the island, fascinated by its isolation amid his element, and here he spent the next few days, lying under a tangled mass of overhanging brambles by day and snail feeding and island circling after the light had gone. No human enemy ever walked this cut-off piece of land. The bankside was as available to him by day as the main margins of the lake were after the anglers had gone. It gave the carp some obscure sense of satisfaction to know that he could lie basking with mouth almost touching land without risk of disturbance or sudden visitation by a figure clutching a rod.

Heat wave over, wind-level increasing, peremptorily dispersing the early morning mist to stroke the water into rippling wavelets, the weather had changed at last. This was good, thought Andy, as he crept through the half-light to the lake that morning. Evaporation had been occurring and increasing each day of the hot weather, drastically lowering the water-level, reducing the inflow to a mere trickle. Water was becoming de-oxygenated, dangerous to fish life, although the underwater spring still flowed at a reduced rate. Rain was needed. Reaching the beach at the end of the track, the boy turned left into Cypry's corner, pushing his way blindly through the sweet-smelling bushes, to cast a floating crust to the edge of the lilies. He was alone at the water today, having left the house before it was light in the hope of an early morning fish in advance of the crowds. He liked it best when the lake was deserted. In his imagination, the lake belonged to him then, the spell being broken by the next arrival, usually far noisier than his. He sat contemplating his bait, blown by the wind into an opening in the lilies where he had intended it to rest, unconsciously absorbing the natural beauty of his surroundings. Andy was still, in his comfortable low seat, inconspicuous, blending with the landscape as a good carp angler should, while the life of the creatures around him, after a short pause at his coming, continued unchecked.

The boy was growing up, developing in human experience and knowledge as Cypry, his favourite carp, was daily increasing his own secret fishy knowingness. Since the poetry incident the boy had kept his thoughts and ideas to himself, becoming even more withdrawn than before, almost living at the lake, his refuge and haven. To his parents', but not his teachers' surprise, his innate intelligence overcoming the lack of mental energy which seemed to typify his nature, he had passed five 'O' Levels this year, announcing after the results that he intended to stay on to take the 'A'-Level examinations in English and Biology. This again disappointed his father, who had envisaged an apprenticeship to his own trade at sixteen. He was more pleased when Andy, closely questioned about his future in the way of parents, replied casually that he had thought of becoming a teacher. This was a somewhat unproductive occupation in his father's judgement, but was better than ending up as a sort of fishing layabout, as he had feared. New pride in his son failed to survive for long. When pressed further for a reason for his decision, the boy had replied that he supposed it was because he would have three months' holiday a year to go carp fishing; having previously decided on teaching on the spur of the moment, under pressure to declare himself for some positive future, Andy felt he had to justify to himself his choice in some honest way. He had long ago given up any hope of a good relationship with his parents. The damage had been done in the early teenage years. They were strangers, their ideas uncommunicable. He had resolved to say and do what he wanted in a quiet way, letting the unreasoning anger and. prejudice break on an apparent wall of indifference.

His unconsidered remark about holidays brought the expected explosion. The father, having worked hard for sixty hours a week for nearly thirty years with an average of less than a fortnight's holiday a year, during which, morose and sullen, with no interests outside his work, he had longed to get back to his trade, was incensed at the very thought of his own flesh and blood admitting to enjoyment of so much time off. The boy had not changed. Andy bowed his head to the accustomed tirade until the man barged off to complain to his sympathetic friends in the public bar of the local about the deficiencies of the 'modern generation' in the way of parents since time immemorial, when he slipped slyly out of the back door with his rod, ignoring his mother's call, going as usual straight to the uncritical lake. To him, work was only a segment of life, not a virtue, but a necessity, to enable him to earn money to do the things he really enjoyed.

Remembering the incident of a week ago while waiting for the fish to take, Andy smiled briefly to himself. After all, the future was his, not his father's ... The broad back of a carp moved near the bait and immediately the boy was all angler. No other thought existed beyond that of hooking the fish which he succeeded in doing twenty minutes later. A five pounder, caught, as he had hoped, before anyone else was sharing with him the pool which he sometimes felt was his. Two hours later he had another, bigger fish; this was developing into one of the good days, he thought, as he ate his breakfast sandwiches. A few anglers had arrived, but none had come near him. All were quiet. He sat on between two bushes, protected from the wind by their greenery. Now he had a long wait. Fish were not feeding. He amused himself by coaxing a robin to take small pieces of bread from his boot. The birds had become very tame here, realizing that most of the anglers had no desire to hurt them or were not interested in them, while they stole discarded pieces of bait.

Most of the time, the boy sat very still and this encouraged a pygmy shrew, which had been enviously watching the bolder birds, to scuttle from the protective grass cover into the inside of a hollowed-out loaf, the crumb of which Andy had removed for bait. Once inside, the little animal was in heaven. With food above, beneath, and on either side of him, he nibbled and nibbled in an ecstasy of eating.

Andy had seen the loaf move and guessing what had happened, he carefully manoeuvred his body into a position from which he could watch the shrew; he could see each movement of the pointed-faced, be-whiskered animal. Only the quiet angler got so near to Nature. Once, while the boy was fishing from the cover of a big hazel bush, a grey squirrel had actually jumped on to his shoulder, doubtless mistaking him for a piece of wood! Discovering its mistake, the squirrel had hastily leapt for the nearest branches chattering with rage at being so deceived. Temporarily sated, the shrew peered out from the loaf, saw Andy, but as he made no movement, it ignored him, darting back into the grass from which it came. Later, a kingfisher landed vibratingly on Andy's rod, where it lay projecting over the water, supported by the forked rod rests. To his delight, the exotically-coloured bird dived several times into the water, returning to perch on the quivering rod, head turning incessantly to watch for food-fish. No carp would take while the bird moved the rod, but Andy cared little; this had never happened to him before, although he had heard older anglers tell of the occurrence as one which was not altogether rare, perches over the water being hard to come by for a fishing bird. To the boy, the chance to observe wild creatures at close quarters was one of the great attractions of this type of fishing, where silence and inconspicuousness was obligatory and where the baits remained for long periods in the water, for fear of disturbing the ultra-cautious carp at each re-cast. If the fishing was dead there was always something living to watch, even if it was only the intelligent ants among the leaf mould, or the dipping flying insects over the water.

This day was not perfect for carp fishing, but it was fairly

warm, with some broken cloud and a slight wind. Andy had
been sitting for nine unbroken hours; it was time to go stalking.
Since there were clearly no feeding fish in the area, he must
go and look for them. Anyway, there was a limit to the length
of time anyone could sit still, however keen an angler. Carp
stalking was the fishing method Andy liked best. There was
great satisfaction in inducing a visibly reluctant carp to take
a bait it did not really want. Fish caught by this method are
usually close in, easily observed. Besides, he hoped to spot
Cypry again.

Changing the spool on his reel for one containing line of
12.5 lbs. breaking strain, compared with the eight pound line
he had been using before, as he had learnt to do from the local
experts, Andy strapped a trout fisherman's hip bag round his
waist, picking up his rod and landing net. The bag contained
seventy bits of crust of assorted sizes prepared the night before,
a lump of bread paste, a tin of worms, a spare spool, hooks, a
disgorger, and some split shot for weights. There was also
a spring balance and a cheap camera, Andy's last birthday
present. He pushed some sandwiches among the tackle, then
was ready. There is no place for large quantities of tackle
with this wandering type of fishing, only the basic minimum
being carried to facilitate passage through the undergrowth.
Slipping silently through the trees behind him, the boy stood
for some time by the lilies, watching for fish movement. There
was none, so he decided to continue. There was an angler at
each end of the beach, and in order to avoid them, Andy made
a detour into the wood, crossing the track and plunging deep
into a pathless wilderness of varied bushes, shrubs, and im-
mature trees, moving quietly in order to cause the minimum
amount of disturbance. He always enjoyed doing this; it gave
him a sense of adventure to leave the well-trodden paths.

Turning back towards the lake, the boy rejoined the bank
at the north side of the same overhanging chestnuts under
which Cypry had discovered the crust on the previous night.
Sweating with the effort of pulling the rod and awkwardly-
shaped net through the greenery, he cast the crust under the
arching branches, then sat to rest. The bait floated serenely
for half an hour, until it was sighted by two wandering coots
which raced each other to the food. Andy drew the crust away

just in time. The birds swam around angrily, each blaming the other for the unexpected disappearance of the tasty-looking morsel. As soon as the bread was out again, the coots, alerted by the splash, made straight for it in competition. Annoyed, Andy stood up quickly, knocking loudly against the nearest branches with his landing net handle. Startled, the coots, which had not previously been aware of the hidden angler, spread their wings, raising themselves a very little above the water like hydrofoils at speed and shot off across the lake, appearing to run over the surface, aided by the spread and rapidly flapping wings. They uttered furious cries as they went; after some fifty yards, they subsided noisily into the water again, resuming their food search.

The boy sighed, reeled in his bait and walked slowly on. He could see another angler in the open swim opposite the small island, but before this there was a mass of old withies growing into and under the water, where carp often lay. Treading carefully, Andy reached the twisted trees, leaning over to look underneath. Yes, less than fifteen feet from him were four carp, lying near the surface, mouths working a few inches from the gnarled roots. The biggest was a fat old mirror of more than twenty pounds in weight, and none of the others was less than ten pounds. Hands trembling, Andy withdrew inch by inch to affix a small crust to his hook. Doubtful about whether his line was strong enough to hold a big fish in such a difficult lie, but reluctant to change it for fear the fish would depart, he wound the bait up to within six inches of the rod tip, then poked it cautiously through the branches. Advancing to lean against a heavy limb he was able to see that the carp were still there, though two had changed their positions slightly. With infinite care he pushed the rod further forward, having chosen a place to the side of the trees where he would be able to step to the left if a fish was hooked, in an attempt to pull it out of danger.

When the hanging crust arrived at a position almost above the carp, Andy released the reel pick-up, holding the line, to lower the bread until it barely kissed the water, descending splashless from above. Three of the fish spotted the bait at once, immediately moving away from the area, but slowly, unfrightened, naturally nervous and not really hungry. The twenty pounder, majestic and confident, swam round the bait three times, then angled towards it, stopping with its mouth almost touching the bread, tail curved for an instant getaway. Then it began to mouth the bait, making it tremble and rock in the still, clear water. Andy tensed. Indecisively, always suspicious, the big fish half sucked the bread into its wide mouth, then expelled it sharply. Like a tiny boat taken by a current, the bread floated away. All four fish then lay for twenty minutes ignoring the existence of the object which hung among them so temptingly. Andy tried to hold his breath. At the end of this time the third biggest carp, a common of about thirteen pounds or so, flicked its powerful tail once, gliding towards the bread, where it backed water, hesitated for an instant, then took in the crust, turning quickly for the haven of the nearby snags. As it turned, Andy set the hook with a short jerk of the rod, there was a commotion among the tree roots, the rod bent dangerously while Andy desperately attempted to prevent the hooked fish from penetrating further into the root jungle, then the line went sickeningly slack. Shaking all over, the boy examined the end of the line. The carp had broken it at the knot, always the weakest point of the nylon. He subsided on to the damp ground, disheartened. He hated to leave a hook in a fish, although he knew that it would soon be rubbed out of the flesh against something hard, and that the place would quickly heal. He had seen a carp landed with two hooks sticking in its jaw, proving that the fish were hardly discommoded by them, but it was bad angling to be broken in this way. It had been his own fault, he knew. Had he stopped to change to a heavier line....

After a while, he philosophically tied on another hook, collected his tackle, and skirting the other angler who had not moved, he soon came to the heavily-weeded shallows at the south end of the lake. There were nearly always some fish pushing their way through the weed forest when a crust placed in their path was very likely to be taken. Here, he fished on until dusk, dropping baits in front of every moving carp, slightly consoled for the lost fish by catching his second biggest ever at nine in the evening. A good day, though, he reflected, as he made his way back to the access track through the darkening wood, among the night-preparing animals. Three fish caught, one fine one lost through his own stupidity, and much peace. He had not spoken to anyone all day, nor had he seen Cypry.

He wondered where the fish had gone.

7 Discovery

Four nights later, long after Andy was asleep, and while Cypry was again feeding on the snail bed, the weather broke, and a fierce August thunderstorm, brought to the lake by towering black cumulus clouds from the west, crashed among the hills. The deep thunder growls, at first unnoticed by the fish, swelled into the lunatic crashing of a thousand guns, the sound being transmitted through the water, to frighten fish beneath. Already restless, unconsciously affected by the falling barometric pressure, the shoals scattered, some to the deeps, others to their favourite holes, where they hid, awaiting what they sensed would come. In the distance, trees began to bend and sway, the darkness seemed to thicken and a loud rushing sound filled the silences between the intermittent thunder claps. Then with a roar the full force of the storm punished the lake. The few huge raindrops, glinting in the weird after-glow of each electrifying lightning flash, became a torrent, a force in the night penetrating the lake water, to rebound several inches into the air, merging finally with the thin rain columns which lanced into the surface. Lake and rain-filled sky appeared to join as one watery mass, whipped into frenzy by a fast-moving wall of air.

At fifteen feet, to which depth Cypry had sunk in fear at the coming of the storm, all was quiet, the fury being absorbed by the water layers above. Cypry rose towards the surface, restless-feeling, unfrightened by the now continuous noise, as he would have been by a sudden outburst. When he came near the top, he felt a strange sense of elation, an inexplicable euphoria which animated him, causing him to increase his speed. This was caused by the added amount of oxygen he breathed, oxygen which was bubble-driven into the lake by the power of the cloudburst, re-vitalizing water drained of its oxygen content by the long heat to a dangerous level, which had already been responsible for the death by suffocation of some small roach and bream. The hardier carp had been un-affected, but now they felt the change, and were glad. Cypry disliked the constant light changes near the surface, however, so after breathing in some of the life-giving fresh oxygen, he started to swim back towards the side he had been exploring, before the island distracted him. Disturbed by the gale, unsettled, the carp realized that he was tired of the island— it was time to continue his journey. Reaching the chestnuts, he turned decisively southwards, determined for a while to ignore the storm.

The sound of rain falling was even louder in the wood. Brushing tilted leaves aside, cascading down tree boles, search-ing out every hole in the ground, the water assaulted the wood. while small animals trembled in their homes and the usually confident moorhens, subdued for once by the tumult, huddled together under the steeper banks. Water ran from everything. waking the roosting birds, drowning many tiny insects, giving life to the thirsty plants. The track became a running river, dust and soil compounded into slushy mud, washed by fresh rain into the lake, to colour and stain the clear water, irritating fish by its opacity. About to leave the cover of the now familiar chestnuts, Cypry paused, irresolute, about three feet deep in water. Water drops were larger under the trees, but had less impact. Intermittently, they increased in concentration when each wind gust shook the branches, re-ducing to a steady drip as the wind passed. Cypry watched the drops impacting into the water for several inches, then dissolving and merging indistinguishably with themselves and the lake, fractionally increasing its cubic capacity. He decided that the constant attack on his lateral line by the vibrating noises was unpleasant, swimming deeper once more, to the peace and pressure of heavy water depths, where the storm was but a memory.

Here he waited, along with many other fish, all moving

uneasily from time to time as if to explore the possibilities
of returning to normal life, like a flotilla of boats penned by
a gale. After some hours of heavy rain, the storm passed to
vex other parts of the country with flooding and loosened
roof tiles, wind roaring between houses like the awakened
spirit of the night. Its passing left a sodden world, silent except
for water sounds throughout the wood, where every surface
strived to rid itself of the fluid which it craved, but not in
such profusion. A damp, sensuous perfume arose, composed
of the combined smells of hawthorn, dog-rose and the many
tangled plants of the undergrowth, mixed with an exciting
elemental mud-smell from the swollen lake, the very essence
of a wet countryside, never smelt by city-dwelling man. Hating
water-matted fur, animals kept in their holes until it became
drier, but great grey and black slugs, accompanied by their
cousins the snails, attracted by the wetness of the ground,
which fed their mucus, or slime, were everywhere. The semi-
liquidity of the soaked grass enabled them to move more
rapidly than usual; dryness was torture to them. Each grassy
patch became a slug's motorway, as the primitive creatures,
monolithic in their impassivity, slid they knew not where at
eight feet per hour, rejoicing in the comparative speed of their
movements.

Some of the slugs would find their way into the water,
tumbling helplessly from the high banks on the east side of
the pool, to be eaten by carp, which were partial to an occasional juicy slug, or more likely by one of the many pike. The
most omnivorous of fishes, the lean ferocious, scoop-mouthed
pike has been known to eat fish of all kinds, dead or alive,
frogs, voles, bread, potatoes, sausage meat, maggots, worms and
almost anything else edible to be found in water, either naturally, or cast in by anglers. The biggest pike at Cartench, which
weighed twenty-nine pounds, had earlier this summer, actually
taken and eaten the last in a line of five ducklings which passed
temptingly over his great head at a time when he was particularly hungry, but this was a rare occurrence. Most hated
and feared of fishes, yet in reasonable numbers a valuable
asset to the ecological balance of the water, pike are often
cruelly treated by ignorant anglers, who, afraid of its sharp
teeth and wicked look, beat it to death, or leave it to gasp

out its life on the bank. Such treatment is barbarous and unnecessary. Like any toothed creature, pike will close their jaws on anything inserted in them. A gag will keep the big mouth open while the hooks are extracted, when the angler need fear it no longer, and can return it unharmed to the water as with any lesser fish, rejoicing at its muscled power and beauty and in the sport it provides for the sporting angler. Even the cruel gaff is not needed to land the pike, as a big net will do the job more humanely.

Careless now of pike or other dangers, coots, moorhens, dabchicks, and three mottled cygnets spread across the lake water, vociferously protesting to one another their lack of fear during the storm, relief at its passing apparent in their harsh shrieks. Water they love, in it or on it, but not the tearing wind-devils which pluck insolently at their feathers, unseen powers diverting them from their set course as they quarter the lake. As the screeches of the birds echoed from the tree tops, a semi-obscured, watery sun climbed above them, and the many fish of all species congregated in the deeps began to move off to their favourite haunts. Attempting to orientate himself, Cypry found that he was swimming straight towards the bank in a narrow corridor of water between the chestnuts and a collection of old willow roots and boughs, where mats of slimy green algae lay. This was the pitch where Andy had had his line broken a few days before. The boy called it 'Smash Alley', because so many anglers were broken here by carp they had hooked, which ran into snags whichever way they bolted. Cypry mouthed the algae, which some carp learn to eat, disliking its sour taste, then swam for a while in and out of the twisted roots which descended deep into the water, learning their intricacies, happy at the existence of such a maze of escape-ways from hateful forces which pulled at the mouths of feeding carp.

Still strangely unsettled, he felt a compulsive urge to keep on the move, as if something was drawing him on, with a promise of some reward at the end, so he soon left the shelter of the willows, swimming steadily on through an area of open water, where the weed had been cleared by a club working party to provide a fishable swim opposite the second, smaller, island. Beyond this, he reached thick weed, the inextricable confusion of reeds, rushes, lilies, shining pond weed and Canadian pond weed which choked the whole southern end of the lake. There was no patch of open water larger than a few inches across in the whole area. The water was at present opaque with millions of suspended particles of soil washed into the lake by the rain and carried there by the swollen entry stream. These discolouring specks were already sinking to the bottom; normally, the water here was fairly clear. What delighted Cypry, apart from the obvious advantages of cover, was the strongly water-borne scent of fish-food which pervaded every foot of this paradise. The smell titillated his well-developed sense organs, especially the four fleshy barbules, which hung, stalactite-like, from the outside of the lower part of his mouth. Dazed by such riches, knowing now what had been awaiting him at the end of his quest, the carp pushed his way slowly through the weed growth, noting with wonder the countless myriads of plant and animal organisms which packed the teeming water. Here, among the stems and leaves of the various water plants, crawling thickly in the rich mud and decaying vegetation of the lake floor, were fresh-water shrimps, snails and fleas, tubifex and other larva, pea cockles, lice, and many other organisms, a feast for any fish. Here, in more than an acre of weed was the secret of the phenomenal growth rate of Cartench fish; here was a feeding ground extra-ordinary, annually self-perpetuating, cradle of some of the finest of Britain's fishes. Instinctively, Cypry knew that he could feed beneath this coagulated carpet for the rest of his life. Abandoning any thought of penetrating further, he indulged in an orgy of feeding for the rest of that day and far into the night, joyously pushing his way through a dim green world, gorging himself into eventual semi-consciousness, to lie, replete at last, in a fishes' heaven, under the stars.

Something unusual brought him out of his stupor around mid-morning next day. He lay still, only a foot below the sur-face, trying to decide what it was. At first the lake seemed normal. His nerve endings gave no warning of danger. He could hear nothing but the usual inane cries of the water birds, wind along the water, the swirls and movements of unfrightened fish. Then he realized that it was the water itself that was different; although he was stationary, the water moved, gently

easing past his smooth flanks where he lay in weed. Although
he was accustomed to surface wind drift, this feeling was not
the same. The water seemed alive, the pressure more regular,
sending against him an almost unvarying, though slight, force.
Little bubbles of oxygen moved around him, entering his mouth
and gills. Exhilarated, Cypry swam off quickly into the current,
searching for its source. Already, the suspended matter in the
lake had sunk to the bottom, causing a fractional shallowing
of much of the depth, and the water was clear once more. The
speed of the flow increased, until it was trickling rapidly past
him. Suddenly, he was aware of a solid mass ahead, and he
turned to investigate, swimming parallel to the obstruction at
the surface. Now he was able to see the actual source of the
moving water, for he had reached the inlet stream, where it
fed the lake. A stone dam, six inches in height, had been con-
structed across the brook where it entered the lake, so that
much of the silt brought down by the flow would be deposited
upstream of the dam, rather than on the bed of the pool, where
it would eventually convert water to dry land. Over this dam
fell the waters of the stream, still swollen with the rain. The
tiny weir so formed mixed oxygen from the air into every drop
which passed over it, injecting its joy-bubbles further into the
still lake waters. Cypry was now aware that it was this
phenomenon which had caused the restlessness of yesterday,
leading him to this end of the lake, and not primarily the great
food beds. Filled with an inexplicable sense of well-being
caused by the high oxygen content of the first running water
he had ever experienced, almost intoxicated by its energizing
effect, the carp swam faster and faster along the dam, turning
in his own length at each end, playing and rolling until his
muscles were aching and exhausted, when at last he fell back
into the weed, certain that he would return again and again
to this magic place. Why go elsewhere? Here there was everything he could desire—effortlessly obtained food, cover,
imagined safety, and pleasing sensation such as he had never
thought existed, among the coruscating waters of the inlet
stream and its weir. For the remainder of that summer and
autumn, until winter frosts chased him back through the now
brown and dying weed to the depths, this was his home.

In September, both Andy and the Expert, who had barely

failed to catch him, had discovered him here.

Andy called this end of the lake 'Crust Country', for he had learnt that when all else failed, carp could be caught here, although very few anglers bothered to try. Heavy tackle was needed to drag out carp which incautiously took pieces of float-ing crust placed in their path, before they could entangle and break the line. It was less sport than open water fishing, but better than catching nothing at all. The boy was most surprised to see Cypry at this end of the lake, and one day he told the Expert so. The Expert, who knew carp, explained how they liked to explore the whole of their environment before settling into a pattern of life, becoming creatures of habit with their favourite haunts and runs. Cypry was clearly doing this. He did not mention that he had been in a position to catch the carp with the scar on its back a few days before, but that he had let the opportunity go by. He had caught one carp of over twenty pounds that season and he wanted another before winter weather made the fishing too difficult. Cypry was not yet big enough for him, though he listened with interest when Andy told him his reasons for being particularly fond of this fish. This boy would be good, he thought, meaning at fishing for carp. He observed closely, and remembered what he saw.

Andy went on to try for Cypry, but was disappointed. Cypry was now preoccupied with the tiny natural foods so prevalent in this weed, and a preoccupied carp is the hardest of all to catch, so the boy had to be content with noting his where-abouts, and learning his habits. After the first week in November, the carp went to winter quarters, and Andy was unable to find him until after spawning time next summer, when he reappeared near the dam. He had spent the winter in the usual manner, and having gained weight fast the previous year, could see no reason for not returning to this happy place.

Who knows how long he might have stayed there, shelving the rest of his travelling, if an unpleasant incident had not occurred soon after the beginning of the next fishing season?

8 Travelling

Len Guud 1985.

A strange thing was in the shallows that day. It was an old, battered-looking carp, white with age in places, dying. The fish moved blindly, lopsidedly, clinging to life. It was unable to see, for perched astride its head, feet clasped firmly over its eyes, was a large male frog. The carp was aware of its age, but thought it was blind. The pressure on its eyes was pain, was part of imminent death. Anglers and naturalists over hundreds of years have remarked this phenomenon occasionally. Some have tried to release the fish, finding that considerable strength was required to do so. It is thought that some sexual urge is responsible for the frog's unnatural behaviour, although this is little help to the suffering fish. Cypry swam past the doomed carp on his way to the dam, giving it a wide berth, as if he scented the odour of death.

Winter, spring and summer were over for another year, the repetitive seasonal cycle becoming familiar to the carp, now in the fifth year of its life. Winter, though less hard than last year, had seemed interminable to him, who longed for warmth, growth, and plentiful food. Spawning, too, was but a sweet repetition, soon finished; following it came a strong desire to revisit that marvellous world of food and pleasure which still awaited him. It was a short journey there, for Cypry had spawned near the head of the pool this time, in other shallows from his own birthplace. As he approached the great weed bed, already aware of the tingle of effervescent water in his bloodstream, he was momentarily frightened into a sharp dive by the menacing form of a swooping herring gull low over the water. Even small birds overhead would cause the carp to flee, when they would have ignored an angler leaping up and down on the bank, shouting. Perhaps some fryhood memory of the danger of winged creatures over the surface supervened; anglers were far away, harmless except through their baits in the water. The graceful bird, hard of eye and grasping but lovely in flight, rode a thermal to high above the lake, where it could watch every corner, to descend again at the first sign of food, usually a piece of floating bread, while Cypry, forgetting its existence, rose once more in the water, intent upon his desired destination. Butting his way impatiently through the clogging water weed, he swam straight for the dam, entranced again by the exhilarating bubbles as they cascaded from the miniature waterfall. Satisfied that all was as he remembered it, the carp moved back casually through the warm surface water.

On the bank, Andy saw the flash of the old scar, realizing that he was once again in touch with 'his' fish. Calculating the distance carefully, he cast his readied crust in front of and beyond where he had seen the carp, raising the rod as the bait landed, and reeling it quickly across the weed to intersect the path on which Cypry was travelling. The carp now neared the stationary bait. Although it was a foot to the right when he came level with it, the bread smell had already reached him. He swam directly to the crust, and leisurely sucked it in. Nothing had conditioned him to caution here. Andy, seeing the crust disappear, struck hard, pulling back with the rod held high. There was a great swirl among the weed, an enormous tug at the rod—then nothing. The line was slack. He reeled it emptily in. Cypry had felt the slight prick of the hook point in the corner of his mouth, had dived at once for safety, and the hook, which had not penetrated his tough flesh past the barb had lost its hold immediately. Andy's rod, momentarily bent into a half-circle as it took the strain of the plunging fish, had straightened quiveringly. The boy subsided abruptly to the ground, knees shaking, assailed once more by that sick feeling which assaults the angler when a good fish is lost. He had struck too soon, as he knew quite well.

Cypry had dived into the thickest patch of amphibious bistort he could find, which he encircled, then stopped. Gingerly, he shook his head. The thing was gone, leaving only a slight ache where the hook had pulled out. Free, but frightened, the carp began to swim purposefully away from the area where safety had proved to be an illusion. He was learning, step by step, that there is no paradise without its dangers, no place where a carp could feed in complete safety, except, perhaps, his secret holt under the old dead tree. He must continue his exploration, but with redoubled care.

At first, in his desire to escape from his latest humiliation, he swam down the west bank that he knew so well, but recognizing his surroundings, he crossed the lake to the far side, so far unknown to him. Here, there was a great change in the configuration of the lake bed. The water was deeper close to the bank, the bottom rockier, with platforms or ledges along which he could swim. The bank itself was steeper and higher, so that he could approach it more closely without fear of running into water too shallow for his thickening body. There was little weed and as far as he could see, few feeding places, although he was temporarily attracted by some overhanging willow trees which held the promise of pleasant shade in hot weather. The hard rocks projecting from the bottom fascinated him. He had not seen anything like this before. He swam round and round the bigger boulders, at times pushing against them, testing their solidity. A thin mat of silkweed covered the rocks, which he tasted, finding it edible, but only to be considered as food in extreme circumstances. The carp glided on, already beginning to forget how nearly he had been caught again, yet aware that something unpleasant which had happened was goading him on. Shortly after leaving the rocks, he came upon a strange object resting on the bottom. It was a sunken, ancient punt, wood flaking from its sides, a sharp stone impaling the remains of its bottom timbers. This boat had a long and sad history.

Major James Wyatt-Smythe's father had ordered it from a boathouse on the coast more than forty years before, and

it had been launched with much ceremony by the whole
family, the first boat on the water for many years. James had
been a small boy then. His father had been keen on boats and
fishing at the time, and had spent many happy hours rowing
around the lake with his two sons. The pool was more overgrown and mysterious than at present, and each voyage was
an adventure. Once they had learned to swim and to row, they
were allowed to use the boat by themselves, thus opening to
them a new dimension in life, alone among the secret world
of the water. Then came the war, their father joined the Army
and the boys were sent away to boarding school in the way
of the upper class English. The boat was used solely in the
school holidays, the boathouse rotted, the roof fell in, and
the punt was carelessly dragged on to the bank after each
trip. Gradually, the once strong timbers, attacked simultane-
ously by water from below and weather from above, became
dangerously weakened, the estate workers who would previously have kept them in good repair also being in the Forces.
One day, when James was fourteen and his brother was twelve,
they were fishing over deep water when James caught a bigger
carp than usual. In his excitement, the younger boy stood up,
stamping his feet hard on the weakest board, which broke
at once. Water poured into the boat so fast that James knew
he would never get the fifty yards to shore.

'Come on, John,' he urged, still jokingly, 'we're shipwrecked!
We must swim for it.'

John, never a strong swimmer, obeyed fearfully, lowering
himself into the cold, dark water. After a few yards of his
feeble breast stroke, his dangling feet became entangled in
thick weed. He panicked and sank before his brother could
reach him. Although James dived again and again, he was
unable to find his brother, so exhausted and shivering, he swam
ashore, then started the long run to the village for help. By
the time the men came, it was too late. The pathetic corpse of
the boy was recovered later from twenty feet of water, and
shattered by the tragedy, James never went to the lake again.
His father was killed by an anti-personnel mine on the banks
of the Rhine during the last days of the war, and at the age of
eighteen he inherited the estate. It was due to his hatred
of the lake that it had been allowed to become so neglected,

until with some relief he had leased the water to the local Angling Society, knowing that at last the place which he had once loved, and where, since his brother's death, he could not bring himself to go again, would be looked after and would give pleasure to many. Recalling the sinking, he had always been suspicious of boats, to the extent that he refused to allow them to be used on the lake.

The sad, sunken shell of the punt had been there ever since, only a few remaining planks delineating the shape of a once fine boat, an inanimate, innocent witness to human error, the drowning of the boy an indirect result of a war which involved many more terrible deaths. Only a few of the older villagers and the Major himself knew of its whereabouts. Fish swam round the remains, silkweed smothered the crumbling wood, and eels made their home where once happy feet had trod. Cypry accepted the punt as another excrescence of the lake bed, yet different from rock and weed which he already knew. Intrigued by its strangeness he spent the night beside a fractured plank, while screech owls split the dark air with their maniacal calls, and rustling night animals quartered the wood.

Next day, he discovered the smaller island, finding little to interest him there now that he understood islands, but while returning towards the lake edge he encountered an odd sensation, familiar yet puzzlingly unusual. He circled, finding again the patch of flowing, colder water which had startled him by its unexpectedness, seeking the place where the clear spring bubbled into the lake. Three hundred gallons of water an hour entered the pool by means of this spring, its flow reduced by a severe drought, but never stopped. Disliking the cold water, Cypry swam away fast until he reached the warm surface water near the bank, surfacing under a tangle of brambles and bushes which grew to the edge of the three feet high vertical bank at this point. Here he basked contentedly, for it was a hot day at last. Dorsal fin protruding into the air the carp lay in the shade cast upon the water by the undergrowth above. He thought that he would be undisturbed, the thickness of the bankside vegetation precluding fishing from above.

In this, he was right, as except for one person, no human penetrated the jungle above. It was considered unfishable by all except Andy, who had made himself a rough tunnel, or

wuzzy, through the dense bushes, the entrance of which he
had cleverly disguised with broken sticks and twigs, and which
he used only when he was sure that no one could see him
enter or leave. On the bankside, he had cleared a space big
enough to fish from, yet where he was invisible to anyone
fishing nearby. There was no other swim within twenty yards
on either side, and the trees of the island hid him from observers
on the far side of the lake. The bailiff, his trained eye noting
a slightly unnatural arrangement of branches, had found the
tunnel long ago. Thinking that he had discovered traces of a
poacher, he watched the place secretly for days, until one day
he saw Andy appear on the path, and with a quick glance
round to see that he was not observed, disappear into the
wuzzy, replacing his cover meticulously from within. Nodding
understandingly, Bert slipped silently away into the trees,
chuckling quietly to himself as soon as he was out of hearing.
He sensed that Andy would be embarrassed if knowledge of
his hideaway was revealed, so he made up his mind to say
nothing. After all, the boy was breaking no rules and good
luck to him for having sufficient initiative to find a pitch which
no one else had taken the trouble to develop. The bailiff was
unmarried, but he had often thought that if he had had a son,
he would have liked him to be just like Andy—a sentiment
which would have surprised the boy's father!

This day, fortunately for Cypry, Andy was not fishing, for
once. He almost wished he had brought his rod, though, when
he saw the carp so close to him, but he doubted if he would
have had the heart to try for a fish today. For this was a sad
day for the boy; he had come to the lake to say goodbye.
He had passed his 'A'-Level examinations without difficulty
and had been accepted by a College of Education in a big city
150 miles from his home, to train as a teacher. Here he would
be too far away to fish his beloved lake except during vaca-
tions, so he knew that this was the end of an era. Three years
later, when he returned to the district—and he had resolved
to get a post as near the lake as possible—he would be a
changed person with new cares and responsibilities. In that
time, small changes, imperceptible to those who knew the lake
less well than he, would inevitably occur; his time here would
never be quite the same again.

He was being sentimental, he knew, but his feeling for this piece of the English countryside was unimaginably strong to those who are incapable of such emotion directed upon a place. To him, the lake had been both recreation and a refuge from a harsh world. The coherency of the fish and animal life on the small estate had meant more to him than parents, friends, home or school. He had developed an affection and an understanding for the inhabitants of lake and woodland which transcended the more practical aspects of living in a manner which perhaps only dedicated naturalists and anglers could comprehend. His years at College would be good for him, making him more people-orientated. Andy lay back on the tough, springy grass of his private clearing, contemplating the microcosm of Nature he was leaving behind him. In the water he could see Cypry, lazing in the sunshine, great mirror scales glinting, accompanied by three other carp, ignoring each other. Below them, a shoal of some thirty yearling roach, silver scales flashing, played in and out of the yellow patches of sunlight which filtered through the bankside undergrowth. Deeper still, he watched a group of semi-transparent fresh-water shrimps, jack-knifing to and fro near the bottom, while at the surface a few water boatmen skidded aimlessly under the hanging brambles. A giant wood wasp, horribly hornet-like, but harmless, and several bees were humming round the white blackberry flowers, and the ground was alive with beetles, ants, and earwigs. Irritating flies tried to alight on his face, while a pyramid of ephemeral midges gyrated endlessly above the water.

High over the bankside vegetation the interlaced boughs of tall beeches spread across the blue and white sky. Sparrows, robins and chaffinches fluttered agitatedly amid the greenery of a million leaves. How could he bear to exchange this soft tranquillity for the discordant reality of a noisy, traffic-dominated metropolis? He knew, of course, that there was malevolent reality in Nature too. Even as he watched, a dipping cabbage white butterfly, flying at random over the lake, was attacked by a huge, multi-coloured dragon-fly, insect monster of the air, which grabbed the helpless flyer in its powerful jaws, attempting to drag it to the ground. Too big to be easy prey, the damaged butterfly escaped repeatedly, each time to be seized once more by the gaping hungry mouth, until the creatures passed out of Andy's sight. Later, the snake-like strike of a marauding pike scattered the little roach beneath him, dispersing them like silver slivers from a bomb burst. As the water flurries cleared, he saw that the pike had sunk to the bottom with a captured fish crosswise in its huge teeth, shaking its head regularly until it could turn the now dead roach, to swallow it head first. But this was natural, he thought; the angular buildings of the town obtruded upon his consciousness. Hideous, artificial, absorbing those who came to them unprepared, draining from them the true life, which could only exist among the fields and woods of the countryside. Others, such as Richard Jefferies, had entered rebelliously into the town's maw, some never to re-emerge into the sunlit land, forgetful of their country childhood, seduced by the wealth and knowingness of the city and its unfortunate inhabitants. Would this happen to him, he wondered?

Then he looked at Cypry, his carp. The fish seemed to him a symbol, a parallel being, growing as he grew, learning as he learned, exploring his watery world as he, a human, must go out into his own. When he returned, the essential nature of the fish would remain unaltered; in the same way, he vowed to adhere to his own inner beliefs, come what may. He would be back, would resume his communion with Nature as before. Of that he was certain.

Taking one last, lingering look at Cypry, who remained unaware of his presence, the boy crawled carefully through the bushes, thorns catching at hair and clothes, nostrils full of the complicated subtle perfumes of the undergrowth. Once out of the tunnel, he hid the entrance painstakingly, then commenced walking contemplatively round the lake, his brain registering each familiar sight and sound, storing them up against a future barren of natural beauty. He stopped at each pitch, recalling nostalgically the fishing successes and failures, remembering every new facet of wild life which had revealed itself to him while he sat waiting, trying to become as much part of the landscape as the great grey heron or the stalking stoat. After circumnavigating the lake, he turned off into the trees, where he wandered happily until the fading light reminded him of other duties no longer to be postponed, then he set his face to the village, home, and preparations for his journey next day.

Cypry, unconscious of the emotion which had washed over him while he lay basking in the sun, sank contentedly to the bottom as the light diminished, seeking a new snail bed which he had scented as he patrolled the area earlier. Day dissolved into black night, its creatures emerged into their unseen, mysterious existence as on every other night, while a young man tossed uneasily on his narrow bed, his dreams not those which he desired.

9 Bream

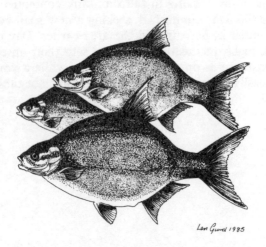

Len Gurd 1985

A phantom forerunner of fast-approaching winter stalked the unsuspecting wood next day. The cold north-easterly wind dissected the circumambient air, capriciously dispersing fast dying leaves through the trees, on to the ground, and into the lake, where they sped aimlessly to the further shore; impelled by climatic conditions from far away icy lands, the wind agitated the still-warm water, carrying with it the scent of temporary death to all it touched. It tugged relentlessly at still healthy growth as if resenting its short-lived defiance to the all-conquering blast. Eventually, the deciduous wood would yield unconditionally to winter wind-furies until leaf-laden boughs became hard bare poles, outlined asymetrically against an alien sky, while the triumphant winds would whistle on, their triumph transient, yet complete. In distant spring, baffled winds would rage in vain, defeated once more by the cyclic growth which annually defied their malevolence.

An intense activity animated the woodland animals at this first feeble warning of coming winter privations. Apprehensive animals, cognizant of the immediate future, began to make their preparation for survival during the long dark months now imminent. Insects would die or mutate, birds migrate or change their habits, and fish, the least affected, alter but their feeding and moving patterns, searching dully for the thermo-cline, eating at random and with little profit. The fishes' cold blood, accustomed congenitally to fluctuating, but always cool, water temperatures, adapts easily to the severest conditions, their self-adjusting metabolisms less trouble than those of the warm-blooded mammals.

At present undisturbed by the cold air currents, Cypry rose to investigate the wind-driven leaf-boats, sucking at them to test their edibility. Disappointed, he propelled himself deter-minedly towards his basking place of yesterday, but the sun was less benevolent today, its warmth dissipated by the probing winds which had already had their effect on the surface layer, reducing its temperature by two degrees, enough to apprise Cypry that this was not another warmth-worshipping day. Sinking deep, where the water was yet untouched by the cold, the carp lay for a while, vacillating. Should he move on or dally? A sudden shoal of questing bream surrounded him, and annoyed by their mindless jostling, Cypry hurried past them, his course decided for him. He swam quickly ahead of the bream, close to a featureless, overgrown bank, unfishable for the most part.

His atypical precipitancy almost led him to appear under the rod tips of a group of anglers fishing side by side in silence in the only open swim in that part of the lake. Seeing their water-distorted shapes so close at the last moment, he sheered off apprehensively into deep water, rising again to the surface when he perceived no hostile movement by the men on the bank. He lay inert, watching. The anglers were intent, unmov-ing. Their baits were clearly visible to Cypry, obviously connected with them, yet with no immediately apparent attachment in the shape of the usual line coming from them. The larger hook baits were surrounded by an enormous pile of similar bready food, and while Cypry watched, the big, bovine bream slid past him, starting unhesitatingly to feed on the groundbait, heedless of danger, ravenous to the point of stupidity. Cypry waited. As he had foreseen, a sudden paroxysm amid the feeding fish indicated that one had been hooked, the shock of its brief struggles assaulting the carp's nerve centres.

The five anglers on the bank were members of the Inter-

national Bream Hunters Specimen Group, often called the
Bream Bashers in angling circles, where many of these specimen
fishing groups, which exist to allow anglers to pool their knowledge of how to catch big fish, have become popular. Three
days ago, Bert Brimmacombe, the bailiff, had been sitting down
to his solitary supper of bread and cheese, and a half of bottled,
when there was a loud knock at his cottage door. Surprised,
as day tickets were sold at the tackle shop in the town, and
the locals knew Bert too well to disturb his supper, he opened
the door.

'William Smith, Secretary of the Bream Bashers Group, and
pleased to meet the best bailiff in England,' said a hearty voice,
and he found himself shaking hands with a short, muscular
individual who was dressed in blue overalls exactly as if he
was off to work as a plumber or something, thought Bert,
which was intelligent of him, as that was what Bill Smith did
on the rare occasions when he was not fishing. He was always
referred to by his members as 'the Foreman', and he ruled them
just like one. He made the decisions, and they did what he
decided, and 'they' were the dreaded International Bream
Hunters Specimen Group—dreaded because they had already
caught the biggest bream from most of the lakes and rivers of
the country, and 'international' because they spent their annual
holidays in Ireland—bream fishing, of course! Bert could see
the rest of the group through the windows of their motor
caravan, a row of grim, unsmiling and surprisingly similar
faces, somewhat bream-like in appearance it seemed to Bert,
and all dressed exactly the same in camouflaged one-piece
Vietnam-type jungle suits.

'Arrrh....' he replied discouragingly.

'Got round to you at last, me old mate,' roared Mr Smith,
jocularly. 'Going to knock out some of them old bream y' got
'ere, starting first light tomorrer. Thought I'd just make your
acquaintance, seeing as 'ow you're the bloke in charge, like.'

Bert didn't particularly like being called 'me old mate' by
anybody and though he was not an educated man, he was far
from stupid, and he knew a crawler when he saw one. This
man was crawling, in spite of his bluster, which meant that
he wanted something, or was hiding something, so Bert's
suspicious bailiff's brain sent out a danger signal.

'Arrrrh....?' he said.

Even the extrovert Mr Smith was a bit dashed by his failure to get across to this man, and there was a long pause.

'Got our tickets, o'course,' he said a bit less confidently. Tickets were business, so Bert must reply.

'Oi'll see 'em in the mornin'.'

Silence again,

'Well, must get a bit of kip, I suppose,' said the Foreman, bravely. 'G'night, Ber.... er, Mr Brimmacombe.'

'Good noight,' and the door was shut before Mr Smith could turn away.

'Friendly bloke,' he could be heard saying sarcastically to the others as he climbed into the van, and Bert smiled to himself. It wasn't his job to be friendly.

Both he and the IBHSG, of which he had never heard, were thinking of big bream that night.

It happened that ten years previously about fifty big bream of a special fast-growing strain had been put into Cartench. For some reason they had failed to interbreed with the bream that were already there, although they had grown. Up to a weight of about 5 lbs. they had been caught regularly, but after that—nothing, and the locals said that the failure to catch them dated from a new rule that had been passed by the club committee a few years ago, which prohibited the use of line of less than 9 lbs. breaking strain.

This rule had been made necessary because so many anglers using very light tackle had been broken in big carp and tench so often that it was feared that these fish, their mouths festooned with hooks, would be permanently injured, and so the rule was made, although not without some opposition. Bert was told to enforce the new rule, and he rigorously enforced it! At first, he used to insist on testing a sample of the actual line being used by hanging it from a tree with weights attached, but this was too much even for the club Secretary, so Bert was gently reminded about breaking strain/line diameter ratios. His eyes gleamed, for he was a little tired of toting around that 9 lbs. weight, and off he went to get a micrometer.

Bert soon learned to recognize the special lines, and to allow for their fineness compared with their breaking strain, and

the micrometer told him if the line was too thin to be 9 lbs.
breaking strain.

As far as the bream were concerned, it was estimated that
there were now about thirty-five of these 'uncatchable' fish,
and that all of them were over ten pounds in weight, with
several around fifteen pounds—well in excess of the current
British rod-caught record. 'Super-bream', they had been called,
and it was said that they would only be taken again on a very
fine line, no stronger than about 2 lbs. breaking strain. It was
fairly obvious to the Bream Group when this rumour reached
them, that it had grown up simply because light lines were
banned, but there was just a chance that it was the heavy
lines which were putting the fish off, and they had set to work
to find a way of getting round the rule.

At dawn the next morning the group appeared silently on
the bank—five dedicated figures, under the Foreman's orders.
At his whispered command, in went a hundredweight of
groundbait where the bream were known to feed, and the
anglers cast into the baited area using their well-known concentration technique which had been so successful on other
waters. Then they settled on their bed chairs and waited.

At 7 a.m., Bert appeared beside them from the trees.

'Morning. Tickets please.'

The Foreman, who had been dreaming of a record bream,
must have mistaken Bert's rasping voice for his electric buzzer
which they all used to detect bites, for he grabbed his rod and
struck violently, nearly dislocating his arms with the force of
the strike, and falling sideways off the bed chair at the bailiff's
feet.

'Cor, you scared the 'ell out o' me, you did,' he gasped,
before struggling to his feet and producing the tickets, all of
which were in order.

'Oi'll test your line,' said Bert flatly, fingering his micrometer.
Every members' line was within the required diameter, but
when Bert had tested them all, he returned again to the Foreman.

'What's this, then?' he said grimly, pointing to the rod. On
each rod, near the butt ring, was a small cylinder, and attached
to this cylinder was a tiny brush, through which the line
appeared to run.

'Oh, er ... a little idea of ours,' said the Foreman airily. 'Contains a cleaning fluid to keep the line free from dirt, etc., and a bit o' soap to help it to sink when we uses light baits. 'Ave a look.'

He pulled out a small rubber bung on the cylinder, and Bert was able to see a milky looking liquid inside. He lowered his head and sniffed at it.

'Want to taste it, too?' asked Mr Smith, winking at his friends.

'I do,' said Bert, with a straight face.

It tasted vaguely of soap, so the bailiff turned away, apparently satisfied, and continued his rounds without another word, and the Bream Hunters kept on bream fishing.

They had a number of tench, and one or two small carp, which took a surprisingly long time to land, and it was 8 p.m. before they took their first bream, which came, appropriately enough, to the Foreman. After a fight it was landed, and it was huge—10 lbs. 13 ozs. on the club scales, weighed and witnessed by Bert, as part of his job. Three more bream over ten pounds were caught before packing up time, and the group looked very pleased with themselves as they passed Bert on the way up to their camp.

The next day they had seven bream between them, and it was the first of these which Cypry had seen caught. Two of these fish were over eleven pounds, and the Foreman was heard to say loudly that they would break the record before the end of the week.

'Not if oi know anything about it,' thought Bert, but he was still puzzled. He had watched all those fish being landed, and he was convinced that the group *were* using light lines—about 2 lbs. breaking strain he estimated from the great length of time they had taken to get each fish in, yet the lines still appeared to be the thickness of standard 9 lbs. line; he had tested twice more, while the Foreman smirked behind him.

Many bailiffs would have taken the law into their own hands and tested the line with a weight or a spring balance, but Bert was a literal-minded man, and it must be remembered that he had been told not to do this, so he had to find a way to put the bream anglers in the wrong. The question was, how could line of the correct diameter for a 9 lbs. test *lose* some of its thickness in water, as he was convinced it must, or the bream would not be taking? The Bream Group had done nothing different from the hundreds of others who had tried to catch the big bream before, except ...

Bert now knew that the key was the brush and the little cylinder of liquid on the rods, though he couldn't think how the trick was worked, so that night he devised a plan to find out if he was right. He had noticed that at 12.30 each day the group reeled in as one, placed their rods on the rests, and walked up to the village pub, from which they returned a few minutes after closing time. They knew their tackle was safe, as Bert was at the lake all day. This would give him 1½ hours in which to work. The next day was a Thursday, the quietest day of the week at the lake, and ideal for his purpose.

The bailiff did a good bit of fishing himself, though not at the lake, for he was the club's star match angler, when he could tear himself away from his duties at Cartench, and he had a huge collection of tackle, much of which had been given him by grateful club officials for his work at the lake. That night he sorted through it, and put aside six spools of the same interchangeable type, belonging to the popular make of reel which he had observed was used by all the bream group. Three of these were already filled with a very similar line to that which the bream anglers were using, and of the breaking strain Bert wanted, and he soon transferred some identical line from two others of his collection of reels to the empty spools.

Next day was fine, and there were only three other anglers at the lake, all carp men and far away on the other side, anxious only to keep away from each other and from the group of strange-looking figures who sat so close together. As soon as the group left as usual for the pub, Bert went to each rod in turn, cut off the eyed hooks, and changed the spools for the ones he had in his pockets. He then tied the hooks on again, threaded the line through the rod rings, and put each hook in the loop provided, where it had been left by the owner. Then he placed each rod on the rest exactly as it had been left, and disappeared into the bushes. It had taken him less than half an hour. Only Cypry, who had returned again to the same spot, fascinated by seeing the big bream caught one after another, saw what he had done, and he was unable to understand.

Shortly after closing time, the Bream Hunters, full of local beer, came talking and laughing down the ancient track, quietening as they neared the water. Without hesitation, they picked up their rods, baited up, and cast out. Still Bert waited, invisible. He made no move until each angler had reeled in and re-baited at least once, and then he appeared by the side of Mr Smith.

'Come t' test your line.'

'What, again? You've done it three times already,' protested the Foreman.

'Come t' test your line.'

The Foreman tapped his head behind Bert's back, and one by one his members solemnly submitted their line to the micrometer. When he had finished, Bert turned to their leader.

'Y're breaking the rules,' he said flatly, handing him the micrometer. Expostulating loudly, Mr Smith measured all the lines twice, and his face went white, for every one was no thicker than an average line of 2 lbs. breaking strain. He looked unbelievingly at the bailiff.

'Out,' said Bert, collecting their permits. 'You'll be reported to the Secretary.' They left meekly, shaking their heads. As they went up the track, silent now, a slow, rare smile spread over the bailiff's hard face. He had been right, and he knew now what they had done. The little cylinder contained a liquid which coated the line, not cleaned it, and covered it by means of the brush, with a substance that increased the thickness, but not the breaking strain, and this coating dissolved in water, and was renewed each time the line was reeled in. So the line was the thickness of 2 lbs. monofilament in the water, and 9 lbs. whilst on the reel!

What Bert didn't know, or care about, was that the liquid, which was called polychromocovaslic, had taken the Bream Group's Scientific Officer who was a research chemist, nearly a year to develop, and was now useless, as the group would never be allowed at Cartench again—Bert would see to that!

The line that Bert had substituted was ½ lb. breaking strain match fishing line, the lightest you could buy, and when 'coated' it was about the diameter of a normal 2 lbs. line, thus breaking the rules. Bert had counted on a few pints of the local beer to make the anglers oblivious to the fine line on their return from the pub.

They found out how they had been tricked, of course, when they got home and tested the line, but it was too late then— they could never prove it. And after all, they had been cheating.

10 Cliff

Lon Gurd 1985

Such small human comedies are not uncommon in the life of a water bailiff, but Cypry was only aware of the departure of the blurred figures on the bank and the cessation of the periodic water-roars which had heralded the hooking of yet another silly bream. Disappointed, ignoring the other fish which still fed ravenously on the groundbait left by the bream hunters, the carp moved quickly northwards, as if already realizing that he was now not far from his birthplace.

He would be six years old in the spring. His length was now over two feet and he was twenty inches in girth. It was past time for him to take up a settled, adult life, which would commence as soon as he had finally explored the remaining area of the lake. But that was not to be this year. Although Cypry was returning to familiar water, as he realized later that evening when he recognized the great snail bed off the large island, a hard frost set in while he fed and the temperature remained below freezing all the following day, and for

several succeeding days. It was, after all, the month of
November.

His vague purpose blunted by his changing metabolism,
the annual death of his comfortable summer existence once
more upon him, Cypry forgot where he was going, and in
obedience to the signals of his body swam dully into deeper
water between the island and the east bank, where he passed
the rest of the hated winter in the usual way, restlessly un-
adventurous and confined.

Existence narrowed by winter monotony, only occasionally
varied by brief excursions into shallow water during mild
weather, Cypry disdained the baits of the few brave fanatical
winter carp anglers who frequented the lake, survived storm,
frost, rain, and snow to a late spring and the accustomed
routines of spawning and heavy feeding which accompanied
the season. He spawned over the island shallows that year,
then spent ten glorious days and nights totally preoccupied
with feeding on the huge snail bed, crunching the mineral-rich
shells in the powerful pharyngeal teeth like a sweet-chewing
child, forgetful of the last stages of his exploratory journey.

It was chance which set him off again, on a lovely morning
in mid-July. The sky was blue, the water warm, the great sun's
rays struck clear to the lake bottom with a golden light,
causing unfamiliar shadows among the feeding fish. One of
these odd shadows stimulated a now satisfied Cypry to investigate its source, and he swam slowly upwards into horror.

The great bleeding shape into which he blundered before
he sensed the foul smell of putrefying flesh was that of an
enormous carp, once well over thirty pounds in weight, with
a huge distended stomach almost two feet below its strained
back. In one side of the mottled stomach wall was a wide
split in the flesh nearly a foot long, through which oozed an
infected mass of semi-congealed blood and eggs.

This was a rare spawn-bound female, which for years,
through an infection within the reproductive organs, had been
unable either to discharge the eggs, or to absorb them back
into its body, and the great concentrated weight of the unshed
eggs had at last torn open the stomach. Fungus and parasites
had attacked the wound, and the carp was dying, drifting
aimlessly through the happy summer water like the survivor

from some titanic battle of underwater monsters. Now and again the stricken fish gave a feeble wriggle in a vain attempt to propel its grotesque hurt body to some shallow weedy place where the dragging abdomen would receive some support.

The carp felt no pain, only a terrible lassitude, and a horrid instability as its bodily functions deteriorated. It would linger on for weeks yet, until it finally died, and the bloated stinking body drifted ashore, a rare corpse in a lake where the fishy dead normally sank without trace at the end of their long lives, returning unseen to the mud of the lake bed, where rapid decomposition soon removed even the bones from a visible existence.

The water-borne scent of putrefaction and the aura of death which surrounded the doomed carp frightened Cypry into a wild burst of acceleration in which his own healthy muscles took him almost at full speed clear across the lake, where his nerve endings warned him just in time of solidity ahead. As he turned, the violence of his arrival scattered a group of smaller carp, which fled in panic at the imagined danger, to return slowly but inevitably by ones and twos, to the spot from which Cypry had disturbed them.

Backing off and at the same time sinking deeper into the water, Cypry looked around him, hanging suspended in mid-water, tiny movements of the fins keeping him stable in one position. He found himself poised over deep water, with a wall of solid rock going beyond the limit of his vision above him. A fractured canopy of tree branches hung high above the water, letting geometrically-angled shafts of yellow sunlight penetrate the clear depths to a rocky, irregular bottom. There was a vague scent of living food permeating the immediate water layers, so Cypry watched the small carp, which appeared to be feeding, although in a most peculiar manner.

There were eight to ten of the fish almost in a line, mouths unusually close to the semi-vertical cliff face, bodies inclined upwards at more than 45 degrees. He slid closer, seeing that the carp were feeding on white maggots which appeared periodically from above, and which seemed to be dropping from the cliff face. Circling deeper, Cypry saw that the bottom of the lake where it joined the cliff was carpeted by the wriggling grubs. Several lithe eels, some tench and a few bigger carp were swimming above the maggots, sometimes angling down to suck some into their mouths.

Although Cypry had eaten the occasional caterpillar which fell from overhanging bushes, these creatures still held a distant but warning memory for him, so he moved cautiously off to the edge of the baited area, where he could watch from a few feet down the bottom's slope into still greater depths.

Andy, who was the provider of the maggots, watched him go from his vantage point twenty-seven feet above the lake floor. He was back at the lake for his first summer vacation after a year of College, and he was preparing for a few days hard fishing on 'the Cliff', as he had named this barely fishable place. There was twelve feet of the broken rock face scattered with the tufts of clinging plants and grasses which had anchored themselves there below him, and fifteen feet of clear, translucent water below that. Two beeches about eight feet apart grew right at the cliff's edge, their moisture-seeking roots causing small ridges in the hard ground under him. The rocky soil was covered by decaying leaf-mould and beech-mast whose rich, ripe perfume gave to the place a distinctive aroma, while on either side of the narrow pitch tangled vegetation made it impossible to reach the water's edge, even though the cliff sloped down to form little more than a high bank.

The first horizontal branches of the young beech trees grew a mere four feet from ground level, which meant that the angler's rod could not be raised in the usual way, but must be angled downwards towards the surface, the strike being made with no more than a flick of the wrist as the line tightened, and the hooked fish played with the rod held parallel to the branches.

A difficult place to fish, but a magical one to Andy, who had perhaps been the first person ever to fish there. To the average angler, it was impossible, but Andy had evolved a technique of landing fish from there, using a long handled telescopic landing net while he hung over the water, roped safely to the trunk of the nearest tree by means of a moun-taineer's snap link. Whenever the lake was crowded, Andy sought solitude here, aware that the overhanging branches made him invisible from the other side of the lake while the inaccessibility of the water meant that no one could fish within thirty yards of him.

Apart from the advantages of the solitude and the sylvan peace of this hidden place, Andy was fascinated by the easy opportunities to observe the fish below. Unaware of the still, quiet figure, head and rod only protruding from the cliff, the carp regularly patrolled along the foot of the wall, clearly visible to the watcher above. Undisturbed by moving figures on the bank, huge shapes glided silently by in the water, and slid over the ledge into obscurity, to return again at regular intervals.

The depth of water combined with the hard bottom made the area somewhat barren as a natural feeding place, but Andy had noticed that the big carp seemed to use it as a refuge, and constant groundbaiting had now caused the fish to see the place as an occasional source of food as well. The bigger fish had seemed nervous of bread baits on the bottom, although Andy had taken several to about seven pounds in this way, so he had invented this method of tempting the carp. Handfuls of maggots were thrown on to the cliff face, where they wriggled into cracks and crevices, many dropping periodically into the water, to be taken while sinking by the eager fish. Then Andy lowered a hook baited with six maggots amongst the feeding fish, with one split shot as a weight to keep the line steady. He held the rod, the bait suspended a few inches out from the underwater rock face about five feet down, where he had caught two small carp by the same method on the previous day.

He had been doing this when an alarmed Cypry had swept into the swim, and his eyes had immediately caught the flash of the old scar as the carp shot past. Now his heart beat more rapidly as he watched 'his' fish lying away from the others, excited as only a carp angler could be by its size and nearness. As he stared, hoping that the big fish would come nearer, he felt an almost imperceptible twitch on the rod top, and quickly returning his eyes to his fishing, he saw the line where it entered the water moving slowly away. At once he struck hard, lifting the rod as high as he dared without hitting the tree branches.

There was a heart-stopping pull at the rod as the fish was

hooked, and the already tight clutch on the fixed spool reel started to click as line was pulled relentlessly from the spool. He daren't let the carp go far, so he tightened the clutch even further with his left hand, and held on grimly. But the new 13 lbs. breaking strain monofilament nylon did not break, the powerful spring of the glass carp rod absorbed much of the unseen fish's strength, and frustrated in its first rush to freedom, the hooked carp dived off in another direction.

Andy felt sick. This was a good one, he knew, and having beaten that first run, it was as good as his. The rod continued to buck and bend, until at times the angler thought the line was sure to break; the fish swirled at the surface, dived once more, but at last it lay tiredly beneath Andy, who leaned dangerously over the water, lowered the big net and engulfed the suddenly frantic fish. Dropping the rod, he raised the long net handle hand over hand up the rock face, until that fine flapping body enshrouded in the mesh was his.

He didn't need the spring balance to confirm that this was his best-ever fish—a gleaming mirror carp of eleven and a quarter pounds, and his first 'double'. Life was worth living, he thought. Freeing himself from his harness, Andy carefully un-hooked the fish, then carried it in the net to a patch of sun-light in the wood behind, where it lay gasping and shuddering on the wet meshes while he took three quick photographs of the carp beside his rod butt. Then holding the slippery carp, he climbed the devious path to the nearest place where he could reach the water, where he returned the fish thankfully, supporting it lovingly until it contorted the great tail and swam quickly away, broad back glistening in the sunlight.

Andy, his hands still shaking, eyes still bright with excite-ment, walked quietly back to the Cliff, looking into the water for Cypry. As he had expected, not a fish was to be seen. After preparing the rod and net, he lay back on the rough ground, inhaling the wood-scent and staring unseeingly into the green and blue leaf and sky pattern so close above him. The wood hummed with shared summer life, industrious insects buzzed and soared and worked among the trees, while below and around him unseen nocturnal animals slept the inert sleep of the exhausted, hidden in secret holes against the over-bright light of day which was anathema to them.

Only ten feet from the day-dreaming angler, unsuspected and undiscovered, a big hedgehog lay curled beneath a pile of last year's leaves, waiting darkness to awaken him. His snuffling and searching for food would recommence at dusk, when he would be little seen by humans, except perhaps when the dazzling lights of a speeding car picked him out as he fearfully crossed a road, scene of the untimely deaths of hundreds of his relations each year.

An errant seven-spotted ladybird tickled Andy's nose, and he sat up to remove it. He had been musing on the contrast between this world of the lake and that other of the College in the city, to which he was now thoroughly but temporarily adjusted, although not, he hoped completely absorbed. Depositing the ladybird gently on a leaf, he peered once more into the translucent water. A few moving shapes below told him that at least some of the fish had returned, so he scattered another handful of maggots on the cliff, and lowered his bait into the water. Then Cypry was there again, a long transient apparition, balanced for flight, watchful but curious. Throughout the remainder of the long afternoon and evening, Andy coaxed the big fish ever closer. Shortly before the under-tree light became too feeble for him to see into the depths, he saw Cypry take a few free maggots, nervously accelerating away after each mouthful, as if expecting to be hooked every time, as indeed the big fish was.

Eventually he approached the baited hook, hidden now by its cocoon of writhing maggots. Andy tensed, rod held tightly. Cypry's broad body, slowly drifting, hid the bait. Then the rod tip vibrated, the quick strike was made, and the hook seemed to hold for an instant before the rod straightened. At full speed, Cypry shot off, while the disappointed angler withdrew the bait, wondering in puzzlement why the hook had failed to hold.

He could never know that the carp had not taken the bait at all. As he moved between the line and the rock, the fish had felt the monofilament along his side, and had quickly turned away. The hook was well below him, and as Andy lifted the rod point, feeling the fish move against the line, the baited hook was jerked upwards round the body of the carp behind the dorsal fin, until by a fantastic chance the bend caught the line above, forming a loop round Cypry's body. Feeling the resistance, the carp swam away hard, the loop slipped over his tail, and he was free.

Disappointed, Andy packed up his tackle and left as it was now nearly dark, trudging the familiar track home through the fast-disappearing trees.

Back in the now black water, Cypry, little alarmed by the incident, as the hook had not touched him, glided easily along the water's edge, on the last stage of his protracted journey.

11 Trap

Len Gurd 1985

The great dark timbers, formless and rotting now, but still held
firm by the encompassing rock, lay far under water in the
deepest hole of the lake, unseen by man since their construction five hundred years before. The action of the water upon
the once-strong oak had succeeded in permeating the wood
to such a degree that a human hand could have torn it out in
great soggy handfuls, but there was normally so little movement in the still lake that a hard core of the thickest timber
remained in the unfamiliar element, small brown flakes
peeling from it as Cypry passed close by next morning.

Seeing the waterlogged wood shards slowly sinking, swirling
unsteadily at his water motion, Cypry backed and turned,
investigating the wood with rubbery lips. It proved to be
inedible, so he expelled the piece he had taken in, and began to
swim towards its source, rising in the water as he watched the
pillar of dark wood set amid the lighter coloured rock like a
tiny seams of coal. There were two parallel shafts, he found,
which came to an end some five feet from the surface. They
interested him little, being too similar to the many fallen

branches and tree trunks with which he was familiar, so he sank again into the obscurity and pressure of the deepest water he had known, intrigued by its difference from the sunlit shallows. His discovery, meaningless to a fish, would have excited an historian or an antiquarian, for there were few of these artifacts left anywhere in the world. The shafts were the last crumbling remnants of a monastery fish trap, built to supplement the catching of fish by angling and netting. The building of this particular trap had caused a great furore in that monastery of so long ago, for the idea was a controversial one at the time.

Although such fish traps were not unknown in rivers, where trout and other river species were less wary than the fish of the lakes, it had been the idea of the sub-Prior, who considered himself a 'modern' in every way, to construct one in their lake and it had brought him into direct conflict, although not for the first time, with his immediate superior, the Abbot. The Abbot was old and testy, conservative in his ways, a monk of the old school, impatient and resentful of his second-in-command, who was young and ambitious, full of ideas. The sub-Prior aspired to the chief position in the monastery, and he made no secret of the fact. Every word and action of his seemed to infer that the Abbot was an outdated old fuddy-duddy who could not last much longer, anyway; the fortunes of the monks would improve, he implied, under his direction. Just let them get rid of that foolish old man. . . .

The Abbot was old, but he was no fool. He knew that this sort of conflict was only too common in the enclosed world of the monasteries; in the past he had been revered as a near saint. Now the majority of the brethren, aware of the probable future, supported the sub-Prior, although not openly, of course; they were still bound by their vows to show respect to their Abbot, to be obedient to his commands. He had bided his time, awaiting an opportunity to discredit his almost certain successor, and to earn himself at least some peace in his declining years, but irritability induced by the bumptious manner of the sub-Prior, combined with his own rapidly increasing senility, betrayed him often, to the open amusement and contempt of his subordinate and his sycophants. Such intrigues were commonplace in monasteries at the time, although unforeseen by the great St Benedict, Founder of the Order, who had considered the religious life so satisfying that there would be no room for petty human jealousies amongst its devotees; lesser men than he had joined the Order, however, sometimes for reasons far removed from the deep Christian conviction of the Saint himself. Many monasteries had become focal points of discontent in the surrounding countryside, the religious life debased, the plump, well-fed monks objects of increasing hatred to the half-starved, miserable peasants. The Order became grasping of land and money, gaining in wealth while the peasants grew poorer. The simple Rule of St Benedict had become modified by monkish 'lawyers', eager for more comfort and an easier existence. They argued, for example, that the Founder had never intended them to take so much time from their devotions to engage in manual work, and this insidious argument had resulted in their being one servant for every monk in most monasteries by the early fifteenth century.

The Abbot of Cartench was a traditionalist, and each day, except on Sundays, at one in the afternoon he led the brothers in silent procession, arms meekly folded, through the cold, draughty cloisters to the fields, formed them into a circle, heads bowed, then intoned the Latin prayer asking for a blessing on their manual work before they dispersed to their various tasks, until the return to the monastery four hours later. Most of the brethren disliked the hard physical work, which the sub-Prior had promised would be done chiefly by servants in line with most other monasteries, when he was Abbot. It was this attitude which gave the Abbot his great idea when the sub-Prior first broached the fish trap plan soon after his return from a six month seminar at Lisburne Abbey, in Ireland, where there was a famous—and successful—fish trap on the River Blackwater.

Now although the monks of his establishment were not aware of the fact, the Abbot had been something of an engineer in his youth, while he was still an expert angler. He knew quite well that apart from the river fish being easier to deceive, the Lisburne fish trap worked successfully largely because of the current, which made it harder for the fish to escape. There was no current in a lake ... At first he strenuously opposed the plan and categorically refused to give permission for its construction. This infuriated the sub-Prior as the Abbot had intended, and the peace of the House was disturbed by furious argument between his supporters and the very few who were still loyal to the Abbot. Dissension even spread into the long no-talking periods and many brothers had to do penance for breaking the Rule. At last the Abbot called a general meeting to settle the matter. White-faced and passionate, the sub-Prior summoned his arguments; the trap would catch more fish in a few hours than ten monks fishing all day; it would fish for them while they slept; it would save much time, and any surplus fish could even be sold to swell the Abbey coffers. The monks sat in silence, but there were few who did not nod their tonsured heads in agreement. The Abbot listened, then mildly, in his quavering voice, once so authoritative, he put his point about the current, for he was a man of integrity, who could not conceal what he believed to be the truth. As he had anticipated, the sub-Prior, loud-mouthed, overrode his objections—what did he, the Abbot, know about it; he had not watched their brothers of Lisburne netting out their huge catches of fish ... !

Even the Abbot's faction was wavering, muttering about 'feeding the five thousand'; fish had become increasingly hard to catch of late, and they were good eating. After some token resistance, the Abbot gave in, suddenly and unexpectedly. The trap should be built; the sub-Prior would be in charge, although he, the Abbot, must have on record before the whole House his fear that it was wasted effort—the trap would never succeed. Ignoring the warning, the sub-Prior left to order the materials and draw up his plans, confident that the Abbot had capitulated out of weakness and triumphant about what he thought of as his victory over the reactionary Abbot. This would further undermine his authority, thought the sub-Prior. By the time the fish trap was working successfully, the Abbot would be the laughing-stock of the House, and real authority would pass to him even before the titular head of the House died; and if the powers-that-be heard of his success....

On the first day the materials were assembled, the Abbot led the brethren to the lake for the first work period, the customary prayers were said, and the construction began. The initial plan —logical and sound so far, thought the old man, was to build a dam across the inlet stream at the head of the lake, then to widen and deepen the stream at the outlet to reduce the water-level in the lake by at least half to facilitate the building. It took five weeks of hard, physical work by the monks to achieve this, by which time they were beginning to wonder whether the sub-Prior's idea was quite so good after all, especially as it was noticed that the man in charge left all the hard work to others, contenting himself with telling everyone else what to do. Once the lake was partly drained, the building proper was commenced. Then it rained, and the first crisis arrived; water started to trickle over the top of the dam. The sub-Prior, whose mathematics had not been good enough to calculate the flow of the stream compared with the time it would take to reach the top of the earth dam, was concerned but not daunted. He decreed they must dig a relief channel through the wood from above the dam to join the stream below the lake. The Abbot smiled to himself, the brethren groaned at the thought of more strenuous digging and the sub-Prior congratulated himself on his ingenuity. Three more weeks of back-breaking labour went by, and the channel—which is still there, overgrown but clearly to be seen—was finished. The diverted water ran merrily through it, the water-level above the dam fell, the lake began to drain, and the trap itself could be started in earnest at last.

Much more hard labour was to come. Two slots were cut in the rock to hold the main shafts of the trap, then a framework was built out into the lake by unhappy sweating monks, waist-deep in water, hampering habits tucked well up. The final result was a high, narrow building like a lift shaft with a sluice-type door on one side for the fish to enter. A platform with a peep-hole in the middle was added above the construction, the total weight of which was supported partly by heavy timbers resting on the rock of the lake bed, and partly by the vertical posts let into the rock face, which had great wooden pegs driven through them into holes laboriously drilled into the solid rock. There was a ladder to reach the platform, and pulleys to control the sliding door. There was even a bell mounted above the platform, to which was attached a rope with a weight at the end hanging inside the trap. When the trap became full, fish should knock against the rope, ringing the

bell. The monk in charge would then release the sluice rope
from the pulley, the door would slide downwards and the fish
would be trapped, to be lifted out with huge, long handled nets.
Meat and bread would be thrown into the trap as 'bait' to
entice the fish to enter.

Ingenious, said the Abbot, when he inspected the finished
construction. The sub-Prior swelled with pride. The brethren
thankfully rested their aching backs, inspected the hard blisters
on their formerly smooth plump hands, and were not so sure.
Three months' hard labour, but if the trap worked ... The
weary monks marched back to the monastery for the last time,
while the sub-Prior and an assistant stayed behind to bait up
the trap. The innovator slept little that night; the hard pallet
in the narrow cell had never seemed so uncomfortable. But
the bell failed to ring, and at first light the sub-Prior stumbled
down to the lake, climbed the ladder cautiously, and gazed
into the dark water below. Sure enough, there was some
movement there. Feverishly, he felt for the ropes, loosened
them, and the heavy door, weighted with a long strip of lead
along the bottom edge, slid into position, trapping the fish
within. The sub-Prior pushed the huge net into the water,
moved the handle around until he felt resistance, twisted it,
then heaved. A ten pound pike, thrashing violently in the
meshes, came into view. It was pulled up, quickly despatched,
and in went the net again ... and again. The final result was
three good tench, two small carp and numerous little bream
and roach, which were too small to eat. A good catch, thought
the sub-Prior, as he carried the dead fish proudly to the kitchens.
When they heard the news, the monks were glad. Their work
had not been for nothing after all, and the sub-Prior had been
right all along; as he said, once the fish discovered the trap as a
permanent source of food, then catches would increase. The
Abbot smiled again; his 'children' were in for a surprise.

And so it proved, for fewer fish, not more, were taken
each day. The sub-Prior began to spend much of his time on
the platform, neglecting his other duties, anxiously peering
into the enigmatic water. Soon it was noticed by those who
joined him, that while many fish swam into the trap, they often
escaped before the great sliding door could shut them in,
alerted perhaps by the noise of its descent. Pike and occasional

tench were caught, but the cunning carp rarely came to the trap, which more often than not was full of tiny roach, bream, and perch, too small to be edible. It soon became clear that someone would have to be on duty at the trap for twenty-four hours a day if even reasonable catches were to be obtained. As this was impossible, even the sub-Prior, wild-eyed and short of sleep, had to admit that the trap was a failure, while the Abbot rubbed his hands together in un-Christian glee whenever he was alone. In public, he said nothing, although it was seen that his eyes often strayed accusingly to the sub-Prior's sullen face, that the prayers for the blessing of manual work became even more protracted and that in chapel much was made of the sins of pride and ambition. The popularity of the sub-Prior fell to its lowest point ever as the brethren remembered the old Abbot's predictions, and their own months of gruelling misery, now clearly seen to have been wasted. The Abbot was treated with renewed respect, and there was peace in the House for his last years, which was all he had hoped for, after all; there had been nothing that was malicious in his actions.

Occasionally, a passing monk climbed the ladder and lowered the trap door, catching a fish or two, and once the bell even rang, as a big pike turned to escape, but this too became rare as time went on. As the years passed, the trap was forgotten, the pulley ropes rotted and broke, and were never renewed, and no food was put into the trap. Lapping, gentle waters and creeping insects eroded the great timbers; wild storms caused unfamiliar waves which slapped at the woodwork like smacking hands. Falling trees crashed on to the structure, which eventually, many years after the monastery itself stood gaunt and empty, home now only of owls and black swooping bats, collapsed into the lake, leaving the two rock-imprisoned shafts to tell of its former existence. Abbot and sub-Prior were long dead, ghostly legions of monks, dispossessed by the Dissolution, marched sadly back into Normandy from whence they came, or impulsively flung off their habits to marry local girls, rather than leave the country they loved more than their religion, and the cowled black figures were seen no more among the woods of Cartench. Local tradition peopled the ruined monastery with phantom shapes of pacing monks bemoaning their lost heritage, and only lovers and cynical poachers went near the place after dark.

In the eighteenth century a half dam was built to increase the water depth, the old fish trap timbers sank further below the surface and were never seen again by man. Only the unheeding fishes knew the place; only creeping water insects recognized the crumbling wooden shafts. Later that night, Cypry rose again from the mysterious depths, passed uncaringly by that piece of ancient history, and disappeared into the autumn night, homeward bound.

12 Winter

An Arctic northerly came to the lake next day, shaking viciously at the summer-laden trees, bent on the extinction of vegetation for yet another year. Its penetrating agitation affected birds and animals instantly with an early winter warning. The sweet smells of summer were soon dispelled, being replaced by the keen hard winter freshness of the cold north wind. Fat thrushes and arrogant robins puffed out their feathers to defeat the enemy, squirrels began to scent the instability of their happy summer existence and a passing fox momentarily halted its silent stalk through the wood to raise its head in salutation, acknowledging the wind's message, recognizing its malevolent intent. Cold was coming.

A lithe black whiskery animal, adapted stranger to the lakes of Britain, entered the wind-shaken water delicately, searching for a fish to eat. As it paddled circumspectly towards a big bed of thick blanket weed between the remains of the fish trap and Cypry's secret tree holt, Cypry himself, swimming fast, was entering the weed from the other side on a collision course. The otter-like animal, a dark coloured mink variety descended from escapees of a mink farm some ten miles away, was the first to stop, hearing the water-sound of the fish's approach. Here came his dinner. Then Cypry, unaccustomedly careless, was upon him, a confrontation appearing inevitable. Ultimately his senses alerted him, and he swerved violently aside, as the mink's sharp claws slashed at his deep body. Unusually alarmed, for a big carp has few enemies, Cypry exploded to the surface where the weed was thinnest and used all his great power to flee at full speed the way he had come. A huge v-shaped swirl disturbed the water as he accelerated. The disappointed mink, whose wild slash had missed the carp by less than an inch, went after him, also at the surface, but without much hope. The animal had long ago learnt that the big carp were too fast for him. Bursting out of the weed, scattering small fish in every direction, the speeding carp dived into the deep hole behind the fish trap, quickly reached a depth of over thirty feet, and shot behind a great rock, to hang apprehensively near the bottom, ready for escape in any direction. The mink was unable to stay under water long enough to hunt seriously for the carp, so after swimming aimlessly above the deep water, far over Cypry's head, it moved slowly off to search for easier prey. Local anglers had been told by the Club Committee to kill any mink they could find, as they took too many of the fish, but many, such as Andy, found the shy creatures interesting to watch, so they left them in peace.

The dark shape had so frightened Cypry that he spent the remainder of the day lurking nervously in the depths. By the time he rose tentatively to the surface later that night, the air temperature was below freezing and the icy wind had cooled the surface water, increasing its density, until it began to sink. Although it was but mid-October, the fish knew from the cooling water that winter was at hand. Made indecisive by the fierce black creature which had barred his way, and by the unexpected coldness of the water, Cypry's purpose was again blunted, and he moved back into the deeper part of the lake, sinking with the summer water, seeking for the elusive thermocline. Fish, with their tiny brains, are constitutionally incapable of carrying through a course of action regardless of circumstances in the way that a human or even some of the higher animals can do, through determination. Although Cypry was now aware, by instinct, that his journey was almost completed, he could not continue against the insistent demands of his annual life cycle. The winter's cold was one of the dominating factors of his existence; and this winter to come, although he was not now aware of it, was to be unforgettable to man and animal alike.

For over a month the cold continued, while Cypry and other carp circled perpetually the monk's hole, until the familiar but hateful lassitude overtook them, and a temporary torpidity stilled their movements. In early December, after a week of higher temperatures combined with westerly gales, the wind again swung to the north, and an even more intense cold returned. The carp were on the move again by now, acclimatized, but as they awoke, the lake began to freeze. Day after day, night after night, the temperature remained below freezing, and slowly the lake water solidified. First the shallow margins, then even the deeps, were coated with the hard ice covering, which was added to every hour from beneath, until there were several inches of ice stretching from bank to bank of the lake. Land birds perched unsteadily on the slippery surface where once only water birds would dare, pecking un-believingly at the cold hardness. The water birds themselves, bewildered, waddled disconsolately among them too upset at the loss of their element even to quarrel among themselves. Shortly before Christmas, the temperature rose slightly, and the first gentle white flakes floated inevitably groundward. The rising wind brought blizzard conditions that night, and more and more snow smothered a white world, blunting the angular surfaces of the winter wood, piling in serrated ridges upon the ice of the lake.

In the uneasy, snow-whirling dawn, the carp rose to inspect the surface curtain which now cut off much of the light from above, bringing a perpetual gloom to the cold water. Some of the bolder fish, Cypry amongst them, slipped their sensitive mouths along the underside of the ice, finding it unyielding, impenetrable. Baffled, the fish spiralled down again towards safer depths as the snow continued to fall. Dull-eyed birds hopped hopefully in the blank whiteness, food supplies buried, while few animals were seen above ground. In the village the road was blocked, and housebound neighbours called;

'Turrible thick, m'dear, bean't it?' to each other from their upper windows. In the hills above farms and isolated houses were cut off from the outside world by the heaviest snowfall this century. Ice and snow weighed down telephone wires until the poles snapped under the extra strain, leaving the shattered stumps looking as though a giant hand had attacked them. Traffic came to a standstill, and the snowploughs were out; it was a cold, harsh but beautiful world. At the week end, villagers began to force their way down to the lake through great sculptured drifts blocking the ancient trackway, which had seen all this before, so many times. Soon Cypry and the other carp suffered a new sensation; the continuous irritating vibrations as youngsters began to clear snow from the ice to make room for skating. Great thuds and crashes from above as the skaters fell echoed through the ice-water, worse to the fish than any air-diluted thunderstorm noises. The constant shocks jarred their nervous systems. Some small, delicate fish, venturing too near the ice while there were people moving upon it, were killed by the shock waves. Carp collected in deep water, sometimes semi-dormant, more often slow swimming, occasionally even feeding under ice as it seemed apparent that these conditions had become permanent. Most were too dull and listless to feel fear.

Andy, returned home on his Christmas vacation, was shocked by the scene at the lake. The bright-coloured clothes of the whirling skaters, the sharp cries of ecstatic children, seemed alien to the quiet lake he knew so well, seemed to mock the life he knew must still exist beneath the ice. He was unable to keep himself from thinking of Cypry and the other carp, as he walked the margins alone, detached from the euphoria of the others. The fish were deep down he supposed, enduring, perpetually expecting the cessation of the noise, the lifting of the barrier which robbed them of light and fresh oxygen. Soon, however, he forgot the fish in the joy of learning to skate among his friends, becoming as heedless and vociferous as the rest. But as darkness came, and people began to disperse to their warm houses, Andy lingered on, peering through the opacity beneath his feet, trying to discern the whereabouts of the fish. He knew that already in shallower lakes fish had died, gasping for the oxygen which could not enter the water through the thick ice. If this weather continued too long such a tragedy could happen here, at Cartench. What a waste of life! At last, he stumped off through the snow in the wake of the rest, sad in the knowledge that there was nothing he could do which would help.

Cold continued, dominated; birds died in their hundreds—it would take some species many years to recover—animals haunted the edges of the village after dark, looking for food scraps, and ponies from the high Moor stood huddled in the streets. The carp became comatose for much of the time, automatically reducing movement to conserve energy and oxygen. They lost weight, living on stored-up food in their muscles; their survival was problematical. The annuli, or rings on their scales would show evidence of the privations of this winter to a skilled scale reader with a microscope. If they survived, the bigger fish would lose several pounds, although spring feeding would soon restore the lost weight. Andy came each day to the lake, hopeful of a thaw, but the end of his vacation came, and he had to return to College, his mind still on the frozen-in fish. In Russia, under extreme winter conditions, carp go into a genuine hibernation; packed close together in mud, they have unknowingly according to the scientists, passed parasites from one to the other, in their state of suspended animation. Unused to such cold, unprepared for the cutting off of light and oxygen, the Cartench carp could not hibernate. Dully, they awoke at times, moved a few painful feet, then stopped again, at one with the frozen, perpetual night. In places, the lake was now solid, a mass of ice from surface to lake bed. The weak and old carp began to die, along with small sickly roach and bream, cold water fishes both, at last affected by the phenomenally protracted freeze-up. Bert the bailiff and the club Secretary talked gloomily on the telephone, now restored, of trying to find the money for restocking if there was a complete fish-kill, as both now expected. The insidious frost cracked trees and great boughs in the wood, and even the inlet stream itself was frozen, the miniature weir a jumble of hanging icicles reflecting the larger ones which were suspended from branches and vertical banks.

The lake was now a dark, airless prison, a dying world. Only the underwater spring brought a little relief to the fish, many of which were now collected round this only source of life. The carp lay quiescent, immobile, unexpectant, while the land creatures sought desperately for food, and died for the lack of it. A great white frozen helmet, beautiful in appearance, but deadly in effect, covered the land, little more than an inconvenience to man, but fatal to many thousands of wild creatures, the smaller species of which were decimated before the thaw. The hibernators, the strong, the lucky, and the torpid, enduring carp lived on. Few of those who took their pleasure on and around Cartench as the bitter weeks ground on through January into February gave any thought to the fate of the animals around them, and the fish underneath their joyous feet, but Andy, far away in the big city, became increasingly depressed. Would he ever again see Cypry, and the other carp of the lake? Were they doomed by heedless Nature to a choking death in de-oxygenated ice-water, they who longed perpetually to swim in summer warmth? He telephoned Bert; there was no change in conditions at the lake.

'They'm done, I do believe, m'dear,' said the bailiff, his voice soft and sympathetic. He, who lived his life among the wild creatures, could sense the intensity of despair in the lad's enquiry.

Then, one day in mid-February, a new breath of wind came to the lake. It was a warm, moist south-westerly breeze, fresh from the immensity of the Atlantic. Where it touched, the temperature rose dramatically; next morning, every surface in the wood was a-drip, and the lake ice was already dissolving, releasing vital oxygen into the water. Rain came, and more wind. Bare grey trees and still frozen earth appeared once more. Ice began to crack, icicles fell crashing and tinkling to the ground, a steady cascade of water ran into the lake. Wide flat ice-sheets floated across the lake, jostling each other as warm wind and rain assailed them, reducing them at last to the water from which they had formed. Rain beat down on a hard world, triumphant once more over its friend and enemy, until brownish snow-slush was washed away, imitation permafrost dissolved, lake water finally resuming complete liquidity. Neither the crashing of the little ice floes nor the influx of the coloured snow-water aroused the carp, but as March came roaring in and the weather continued mild, the water temperature of the newly oxygenated liquid began to rise, and the fish began to stir. Slowly they wriggled their fins and tails, grown stiff from lack of use. Slowly they recovered their atrophied senses, renewed animation bringing its first problem; food. The carp felt hunger. They began to move off from the crowded depths in all directions, uncertainly at first, then with increasing urgency, like a crowd dispersed by a central incident. But the food they sought was scarce, much of the life of the lake having been killed by the cold. Aquatic plants, starved of light, could not survive such a winter, so some of the Cartench weed beds were never seen again. The carp swam aimlessly, quartering the lake, seeking food, any food, Cypry amongst them. The annual miracle was at hand, however, and when a warm spring sun eventually irradiated the lake, photosynthesis could commence again, water weed begin to grow, and its dependent creatures to proliferate. As if to compensate for that bitter cold, spring was warm and early that year, buds and shoots sprouted rapidly, the surviving birds sang again, and the woodland creatures resumed their busy lives, restoring energy dangerously depleted over the past grim months.

Andy came happily again to the lake, helping the bailiff to remove some of the dead fish; mortality had not been more than fifteen to twenty percent, they estimated.

Cypry, one and three quarter pounds lighter, but still strong, fed as never before that spring, his universe a tomb no longer, his life-force restored by circumambient warmth, relayed to the water from the ten thousand mile high flames of a gaseous star, ninety three million miles away in space. As he frantically fed, ever searching for new energy sources, he moved unconsciously nearer to his ultimate destination.

13 'Twenty'

One day in early summer Cypry, temporarily resting from an orgiastic eating bout which had lasted several months, during which time he had more than regained his lost winter weight, looked about him, and found himself beside Andy's 'monster', the great fallen tree which had formed his secret retreat when he was a very small carp. Unaware, he had travelled the final distance from the monk's fish trap to familiar waters during spring, although spawning and much wandering in search of food had supervened. Cypry swam between the water-bleached branches into his old holt, remembering; it all looked so much smaller now, but there was still room to spare even for a fish as big as he. For Cypry, at the start of the eighth year of life, was now the carp angler's dream—a twenty pounder. In fact, he weighed twenty-five and a quarter pounds, and was nearly thirty inches long, with a girth of twenty-six inches. Apart from the scar on his shoulder, his body was unmarked, in excellent condition. The great scattered mirror scales shone in the sunlight; a young fish for his weight, he was perhaps at his fastest and most powerful. As he grew older, the abdomen would thicken, he would become more ponderous with less speed, although the power would remain. Recognizing the proximity of the tree to his birthplace, but reluctant to leave its cool shade, the big carp hung almost motionless in the pellucid water, gills pumping, mouth opening and closing, paired pectoral fins moving slightly for balance.

The dark, ice-solidified lake of the previous winter was but a memory; all was warmth and light again. Carp fry shot continually in and out of the weed stems, rocketing into shelter at the approach of each larger shadow, each water-transmitted danger signal. A few late mayflies danced erratically their final short hours of life away over the wavering marginal weed beds, while on land all was re-birth and growth once more. Young cheeping birds fluttered deliriously on nest edges, possessed by a delicious fear of their first flight into the unknown; animals gave birth in secret tunnels in the earth and the multitudinous insects abounded. Summer sun's rays, their narrow paths delineated by a trillion dust motes, struck hotly through the leaf cover, bringing a golden radiance to the spectroscopic colouring of branches, leaves, grass, and the pure white delicacy of ten thousand wood anemones beneath. Never had the benevolence of summer seemed so sweet to Cypry. Although not aware of the continuity of renewed life around him, the carp could sense the sharp contrast between the cold dead lake of the past winter, and the heat-bred teeming life which surrounded his holt today. Ecstatically, he basked in the sunlight, luxuriated in the warmth, fed in the darkness and moved in a lasting trance of well-being, confident and secure in his strength and his hidden stronghold. Even the arrival of the anglers that year disturbed him little. He ignored the various offerings, now so familiar to his senses, and only ventured out from the tree holt to feed when the disappointed anglers had obediently departed, leaving the night to the nocturnal creatures which obeyed no rules, but those dictated by their need for survival. On a warm July night, when the darkness and the fading human voices had told Cypry that it was safe to emerge, he scented a new type of food as he swam leisurely through the sloping wood-walls of his hideout, stopping occasionally to brush off a black leech which had been clinging to his body. The carp turned, angling downwards through the still water, until the extended protractile lips came into contact with a piece of the unfamiliar food, the scent of which had distracted him. The lumps of food were large,

fibrous, and quite hard; there were a number of them. Cypry
mouthed a piece, enjoyed its taste and finding nothing wrong
with it, sucked it into his throat, where the meshed pharyngeal
teeth mashed it to pulp before it was drawn into the stomach,
ready for digestion. Knowing no danger in the darkness, Cypry
moved freely along the lake bed, tail up, feeding avidly on
each juicy morsel he discovered.

The new food, not introduced into the lake until now, was
potato, each separate ovoid taken from a can and thrown
carefully into the water alongside the big tree by a silent
dark-clad angler who now sat tensely by his rods some twenty
yards to the south side of the tree. This man was not only a
poacher, but he was also a carp stealer. A carp of twenty
pounds is worth nearly £5 a pound today, which is why the
stealing of carp from waters is more prevalent than might be
imagined, but this angler was not interested in the money. He
was an egotistical young man, anxious for fame in the narrow,
competitive world of carp fishing, so he had persuaded a farmer
to lease him a tiny, half-acre pool inconspicuously hidden in
the centre of a lonely copse near his home, some sixty miles
from Cartench. Here he intended to place a few very big carp,
either bought from fish farms, or stolen, which he then planned
to catch again and again, without divulging either the location
of the water, or the fact that each new 'twenty' he took was
one of only five or six fish in the pond. He would catch and
recatch them, he thought, photograph each one from different
angles, 'cook' the weights slightly, and report them to the
angling Press as if they came from different waters, thus
building an artificial reputation as a prolific catcher of an
enormous number of twenty pound carp in each season. Then
he would write about them, describing in fictitious detail the
crafty methods, ingeniously concocted baits and the difficult
waters from which the fish were taken. Secrecy would be no
problem, as this was expected of successful carp men. He
would become famous, would be constantly referred to as
'Britain's leading carp angler', replacing in the minds of the
general angling public the long established genuine top carp
men of the present; and perhaps eventually, he would even
write a book ... So dreamt the poacher. Angling, like most
sports, has its heroes, and he would be one of them, the easy

way; some unfortunate twist in his character prevented him from seeing that the only person he would be cheating would be himself.

He had gone to considerable expense to achieve his ambition. A specially converted van, now parked in a leafy track a half mile from the lake in the opposite direction from the village, contained two large plastic dustbins held firmly by thick straps into recesses made in the floor of the body, while two oxygen cylinders, from which the essential gas bubbled into the water through tubes inserted into the lids, provided reasonably safe transport for the captured fish. The carp stealer had selected Cartench for his first effort, as it was well known that if only it could be fished at night ... Once Bert the bailiff was safely ensconced in his cottage, the angler slipped slyly through the trackless wood, carrying the minimum of tackle in case a quick getaway was needed. This tackle consisted of one rod and reel, the usual accessories and baits, and a huge, open-weave sack for transporting the fish to the van. All but the rod were carried on his back in a rucksack. He knew the water and the surrounding woods well, having often fished there legitimately by day, and explored the neighbourhood, and he had seen large carp moving under the big tree.

When he arrived silently at the water's edge he walked carefully to his chosen pitch, ignoring the rustlings and sounds of the wild night life around him, expertly prepared his tackle, threw about ten small tinned potatoes into the water close to the tree, then baited up with an identical potato, and holding the rod in his right hand pointed towards where he wanted the bait to land, he took the bait gently into his left hand and threw it accurately into the baited area. The line peeled from the open spool of the reel, then stopped as the potato fell into the water with a quiet plop. The angler pushed the rod point into the water to sink the semi-buoyant nylon monofilament, tightening the line until he could just feel the weight of the potato where it lay on the bottom in five feet of water, set his rod in two rests, and sat down. Then he placed a cylinder of silver paper on a Vee of line hanging between the butt ring and the reel, and sat down to wait. The night was clingingly dark—he had deliberately chosen a moonless period—and almost silent, only the occasional movement in the undergrowth betraying the existence of a passing creature bound about its business, and the odd angry squawk of a quarrelsome coot from over the water. In the first half hour there were several quick twitches at the indicator, caused, the poacher knew, by small fish 'knocking' the bait. The silver paper began to jump jerkily towards the butt, the line began to run slowly out from the spool; Cypry had taken the potato unsuspectingly into his mouth, then moved off in search of another. Instantaneously the angler struck, hard, a simultaneous movement of both hands which turned the reel handle to engage the pick-up with the left hand, while the right gripped the rod butt, and the taut forearm whipped the rod upwards. Resistance was solid, but rapidly mobile, as the hooked fish used every ounce of its power to escape. The angler had relied on his heavy, 18 lbs. breaking strain line, combined with a tight clutch to hold the fish, but he had forgotten that normal monofilament line stretches about one yard in every ten, and that a doubled rod will allow a big carp to gain those few extra feet which mean safety. Cypry dived powerfully into the sheltering tree, between two of the supporting semi-vertical branches on the far side, then circled quickly up and over the upper side of the sloping trunk, where he was brought up short by the ultra-taut line which held the big hook protruding from the left hand corner of his mouth.

The angler cursed as he felt the line go solid. The rod was bent into a huge bow, the line twanged from time to time, as Cypry, tethered and temporarily exhausted by his immense expenditure of energy over a short space of time, moved feebly against the pressure which held him firmly, mouth down, against the hard wood of the tree trunk, tail at 45 degrees above him. Stalemate. The angler pulled at the line until it almost reached breaking point, but Cypry, aided by the line wound round the branch, was immovable. Forgetting his vow of silence, the angler said to himself savagely : —

'Blast it; a good fish, too. One chance, now. I must slacken the line, and hope for the best.'

This is a last resort in such a situation; sometimes the fish will disentangle itself when it feels the release of pressure, but more often the hook will slip from the mouth, where it has only been held by the tight line. As he hesitated, aware that this method usually fails, Cypry, his strength recovered, lashed his enormous tail, contorted his powerful body into a half circle, and with one great effort tore the hook through the flesh of his mouth as he straightened his body with all his stored power against the solid resistance of the line around the branch, which, unlike a fishing rod, did not bend to absorb the pull but remained rigid. A whirlpool-like boil, visible even in the darkness, appeared above the trunk where the power of Cypry's tail, operating only six inches from the surface, had displaced the water, while the angler felt the line give for an instant, then become once more immovable. The sharp hook, impelled by the rod's spring, combined with the elasticity of the freed line, had been projected from Cypry's mouth with considerable force and embedded itself deep into the unyielding branch, from which no amount of tugging would release it. Eventually, the angler realized that the carp had escaped, and winding a handkerchief round his hand, he broke the line at the hook knot, then subsided unhappily on to the bank. When he roused himself from his fruitless self-recriminations some ten minutes later, he found that all was still quiet around him, so he tied on another hook, moved along to the next pitch, away from that hateful tree, and cast in again, hopefully. By two in the morning there were carp of fourteen and sixteen and a half pounds in his sack—not as large as he had hoped, but they would do for a start—so he packed up his tackle, dextrous even in complete darkness, lifted the heavy dripping, thrashing sack from the water, wrapped it in a waterproof groundsheet he carried for the purpose, and made for his car. With frequent rests from the dragging weight of the water-soaked sack and thirty pounds of carp, and with the essential use of a small torch in the later stages, he found his weary way back through the dark wood to his van, transferred the carp to the water-filled dustbins, one in each, started the oxygen supply, got in, and drove away.

He had meticulously selected a cross-country route to his pond, through quiet lanes where it was unlikely that he would be stopped by a suspicious police patrol, ever alert for strange happenings at night, but he had not allowed for one thing—breakdown. About five miles from Cartench he heard an odd cracking sound, and the red warning light on the dashboard came on. Optimistically, he ignored it for a few minutes, but the rapidly rising engine temperature warned him that a seize-up was imminent, so he stopped the car, and investigated. As he had thought, the fan belt was broken, and he carried no spare. What to do? He quickly eliminated the idea of calling a motoring organization, as the patrolman would inevitably spot the dustbins, the sides of which ran with water which escaped from the lids, and the oxygen cylinders, and might well connect them with the proximity of a certain famous lake. There were no all-night garages in the vicinity; it would be nearly five hours before one would open. He doubted if the oxygen would last that long. Starting the engine, he found that he could go about a mile before the engine temperature rose to a dangerous level; then a long rest was necessary before he could resume his spasmodic journey. In this way, he proceeded for the rest of that long night by starts and frustrating stops, while the life-giving oxygen slowly trickled away into the water, and the captured carp moved sluggishly in their con-fining prisons.

By 7.30, he had parked in a lane four hundred yards from where it joined a main road. There was a garage at the junction, he knew, and he was there as the owner was unlocking the petrol pumps. The man looked up, surprised to see a walking customer at this time of the morning;

'Broken fan belt,' said the wild-looking figure, tersely. 'Got any?'

'What type?' replied the garage man, after a pause in which he looked his visitor up and down.

Of course, they did not stock fan belts of the right type, and the poacher felt like crying. What could he do, then? Well, if it was really urgent, said the garage proprietor, looking at him curiously, he could send his assistant to the nearest town on his motor cycle, but he'd have to pay ... Reassured by the sight of some money, and by the story that his odd customer had broken down after a night's fishing—all anglers were mad, anyway—the man told him that the lad would be here soon. He came roaring up at 8.30, but it was after ten o'clock before he was back with the right fan belt. The angler took it, almost threw the exorbitant amount of money at the garage man, and ran off down the road. Got a nice young wife wondering where he's been all night, thought the man, and dismissed the incident from his mind. Although he knew how to fit a fan belt, it was not as easy as he had thought, and although the angler drove the fifty remaining miles to his pond as fast as he dared with the great weight of the water-filled dustbins making cornering dangerous, it was almost one in the afternoon before the van bumped slowly up the track to the tiny pool. He knew the oxygen had given out long ago; he just hoped that there was enough in the water to keep the fish alive. But it was too late. The carp had exhausted all the air in the water, and were floating sadly on their sides, their short lives unnecessarily ended by the stupidity of their captor. The larger fish still breathed faintly, but it never recovered, and the carp stealer had to bury them both amongst the trees which surrounded a pond far from their home, innocent victims of his unprincipled greed for fame.

So the old oak which formed Cypry's holt, once the proud home of numerous insects, birds, and squirrels, had unknowingly performed a vital function long after its death. The solid rigidity of its wood had saved Cypry's life, for without its uncaring assistance the strong line would have held him, and he would have joined the smaller carp in their earthy grave. As soon as he had felt the hook torn from his mouth, and the welcome release of the pressure, Cypry had accelerated rapidly away from danger in the direction in which he was facing, and buried himself in a thick weed bed, where he lay unmoving for a while. The big carp was unhurt except for one corner of his mouth where the hard wire of the hook had split the flesh for an inch until it pulled out of the mouth. The tear would soon heal, although unevenly, leaving the fish with a slightly deformed mouth at that side, second of the injuries caused by hunting man to his body. With an animal, this would constitute cruelty; to a fish, which belongs to a lower order of creatures, this is not so. An expert fishery biologist has said that neither fear nor pain are experienced by fish, as a fish has the sensory nerve endings which perceive pain concentrated in the skin. With no nerve endings to record the pain the fish cannot feel it, which explains why fish will continue feeding with large hooks in their mouths and gullets, why they are sometimes caught several times in one day and why a shark will feed happily, unaware that other sharks are tearing at its entrails. The part of the brain which in higher animals records pain is also missing in fish, which have no pain-recording apparatus; their attempts to escape when hooked or handled are but reflex actions. Fishing cannot then be correctly called cruel, but the treatment of fish once they are out of water is important. Keeping them in nets, throwing them back into the water, and careless handling which removes the protective coating of mucus may cause damage, disease, and death. The angler has no logical defence if he treats fish in this way, but if he touches his fish with wet hands, and returns them gently and as soon as possible to the water, then he will have done them no harm, and can continue his harmless sport with a clear conscience knowing that those who accuse him of cruelty are those who are ignorant of fish biology.

Fish with these injured mouths are not unusual in this time of so many anglers. Far worse wounds have no effect on the life and feeding capacity of the fish concerned. As he lay recovering from his efforts, glad to be free, Cypry became aware of a familiar sense impression, an awareness that he knew this place, not from recent experience, but through some acute but distant memory of long ago. Curiosity overcoming the fast receding shock from recent events, the great carp slowly freed himself of the enveloping weed with little tired movements of his body, swimming sluggishly into some open water nearby. And then at once he knew; he was within a few feet of the potamogeton bed where he had been born, where he had spent much of his quicksilver fryhood. Slowly, but with increasing pleasure, he moved towards his actual birthplace.

Cypry the carp had returned to his beginning-place; the long, adventurous journey was over at last.

14 'Thirty'

Tips of water-drenched weed, summer sun-soaked, now autumn-dying, were touched with brown next day as Cypry excitedly rediscovered the world of his fryhood, long forgotten, yet dimly recalled in his tiny subconscious. Sedges and rushes withered fast, their seasonal growth abruptly terminated by the first intimations of winter, their intersecting secret water channels still traversed by the silent-paddling bank voles, midget submarines of the lake, whose frantic gnawings helped to decimate the disappearing weed shoots, and whose soft, dark brown coats matched the fading colours of the water plants. The bubbling wake behind the busy voles' water-tracks showed silver in the early morning light, and bubbles spread too from their sleek fur as they swam. Cypry ignored their frantic crash-dives as he slowly passed, reintegrating himself with the faint memories of this part of the lake, unseen for so long.

The low-angled shafts of an autumnal sun chased the last spirals of morning mist vapour from the steaming surface. The thin tendrils of mist rose silently from the still water, to be dissolved and dispersed by the sun's warmth, disappearing a few feet up as if they had never been, like a thousand insubstantial water-spirits escaping after a night of revelry amongst the dancing reflected stars in the ebony water. Sharp cries of active water-birds punctuated the massed cacophony of the dawn chorus from the surrounding trees and bushes. The jungle-like screech of a jay gave warning to all in the wood that an early angler was coming down the track, intent on sharing the delights of a fine morning with the non-human population of lake and copse. A cadaverous heron craned his long neck in anticipation of the man's approach, swivelling his beady eyes for the first sight of the enemy, then relaxing as the footsteps of the angler moved away to the far end of the lake. A moment later the heavy body of Cypry, nosing into the shallows where the hungry heron stood, almost collided with the stalk-like legs of the fishing bird causing the heron to move quickly towards the bank. Head turning suspiciously from side to side like a snake about to strike, the heron tried to keep its dignity as it retreated, lifting each foot above the surface, and lowering it gingerly to the bottom. The wash of Cypry's turn made the bird hurry unduly, putting one leg in front of the other so rapidly that it failed to allow for a deep hole, and toppled comically sideways into the water. With a melancholy honk, it raised its soaked feathers, shook them, bent its skinny legs and took off awkwardly. Already wet, the heron landed unusually in the middle of the lake, where it impelled itself to the further bank like the caricature of a swan. There it resumed its dainty walk, until it found a suitable fishing place, where it returned to instant immobility.

The big carp had turned because of the rapidly shallowing water, not in alarm at the heron's movements, which his eyes had not seen. He was re-investigating this end of the lake, oblivious to the beauty of the morning, his water-sight aware only of things of interest to a carp. He located long-forgotten feeding beds full of water snails and tubifex. He patrolled the margins, emerging and re-emerging through certain holes in the weed beds which he would use regularly in his future life. All that day Cypry moved purposefully in the lake corner, preparatory to taking up permanent residence there, except for retreats to the deeps in the cold of winter and periodic visits to other parts of the water when occasional restlessness and half-recalled pleasures lured him back to journey-discovered haunts. He would become more indolent now, burning less energy through movement, so his rate of growth would increase still further. He was capable of growth for at least ten more years—time enough to become the monster of the lake, the biggest carp of them all. He would establish a regular feeding pattern, but only at night, when the shores of the lake were empty of humans. During the daytime, he would lie unmoving under weed or sunken branches, sun-basking, or would slide unhurriedly into the centre when disturbed. He would often be seen, but never caught, for he had learned by bitter experience of the dangers of careless feeding. Any edible object large enough to contain a hook would be examined exhaustively, possibly even for several hours; if there was any doubt, it would not be eaten. Why should he take a risk? There was natural food enough in the pool, so why be tempted to take that which clearly was not natural, however delicious the scent it exuded? So Cypry settled as a permanent resident of the narrow, weed-choked northern end of the lake where he had hatched, as is the custom with many large lake fish.

He came to know intimately every weather-induced water mood of his chosen home area, each variation in depth, the thickness and amount of cover in every weed bed and sunken tree-shelter. He pushed his way through an aqueous mass of semi-liquid mud covered by but a few inches of water into the first reaches of the outlet stream, where he felt again the moving current which had so intrigued him near the dam at the head of the lake. Often he lay, partly out of water amidst the muddy weed jungle of the outfall, watching anglers as they crossed the rickety old wooden bridge over the stream, staring unseeingly at the restless reed warblers as they sang meaninglessly in the bulrushes so close above his still head. The hollow footsteps of a person crossing the bridge became a familiar sound to him; he seemed attracted by the sight of the men suspended above him by the frail structure of the footbridge.

It was here that Andy saw him next summer when he returned as usual to the lake during the long vacation. Now grown into young manhood, wiser and more confident, ever learning like the great carp, Andy was once again in paradise, which meant, for him, Cartench Lake. The peaceful atmosphere of the little estate, essentially unaltered by the passing years, yet with minimal differences apparent to the perceptive, enchanted him more, rather than less as a result of his enforced absence. At first, he was content to dream in the sun, absorbing again the sights, sounds, and smells of the countryside, letting the cumulative tensions of urban life drain from his mind. Then he began to wander at random beside the gently rippling water, occasionally smiling briefly to himself as he passed a well-remembered pitch, greeting cordially but absently anglers he knew, but with most of his thoughts directed towards the wild life around him, seen and unseen. This was his true world, not that other; in one more year he could apply for a teaching post in some rural school nearby, so that in his spare time, the lake would once more be his.

When he reached the bridge at the north end, he paused above the trickling stream, staring unseeingly along the length of the lake, reversed green trees reflected in its tranquil surface, until a water movement caught his eye. Immediately alert, like any angler, his meditations instantly forgotten, Andy looked into the water and saw Cypry. As he recognized the fish, he experienced a sensation of great joy and relief; 'his' carp had survived the cruel winter and had returned to him. He watched the fish for a while, fascinated by its patient immobility. Then some imagined danger disturbed it, it turned away and Andy was able to see the enormous size to which it had grown since he last saw it. With an audible gasp, he started away from the bridge, half-running up the track to the house for his tackle. When he returned to assemble the rod with trembling, clumsy hands, Cypry had gone. The angler fished on until dusk, so statue-like beside the wood of the bridge that a great brown water vole, identifying him almost too late as a human, made a violent retreat over the moss-covered tree stump he had climbed beside the man, and tumbled sideways into the water with a surprised splash. The noise made Andy look about him, realize it was almost dark, and that he would be in trouble with the bailiff unless he left at once, and he started to pack up his tackle, hopeful that the next day he would find Cypry again.

For the rest of the holiday the young angler stalked his fish, but without success. Cypry ignored him and although Andy caught other carp, the one he really wanted continued to elude him. In late September, Andy returned to College, sad at leaving, but contented with the memory of long happy hours at the waterside he loved. The time of falling leaves had come again to the wood, to be followed by yet another cold-water winter.

Cypry's years seemed to telescope once he had settled to a regular, habit-ridden existence. Winters were but dimly recalled, while he lived for the caressing sensation of warm waters past his scales. The repetitive cycle of the season's changing flowed past him like the river of time; alarms were rare, but he saw much as the years passed. He saw tiny fluffy moorhen babies, cheeping plaintively, take to the water for the first time, their insistent calls permanent distress signals to the anxious mother; he saw the incessant coot-quarrels, the hunting mink, the greedy seagulls and the dart-like, diving kingfishers. He saw trees waving in winter gales and nodding in summer breezes. Once he heard a strange ululating sound and lay watching as mud-spattered hounds and heavy-hoofed horses thundered wildly down the track, the bright colours of the riders' red coats clearly visible to his vigilant eyes. One year there was a great flood, and he saw his liquid tranquillity merge with masses of tawny, gill-irritating water which poured down the inlet stream, until its opacity rendered his world almost unrecognizable. That summer, as the water rose, Cypry was able to swim into runnels and ditches among the trees where he had never been before, as the flood reached unheard-of levels, and fish swam for the first time in the long forgotten monk's relief channel, normally an unrecognized depression, leaf-choked and waterless. Rain seemed never to stop that summer, spoiling much of the enjoyment of the season by cooling the water unpleasantly at a time when it should have been warm and comfortable, making fish restless and uneasy.

Above all, Cypry saw the anglers—and they saw him. At the age of fifteen, he weighed well over fifty pounds, and still he grew, until he was more than forty-two inches in length, a foot across the back, and of an almost unbelievable depth. When he reached the age beyond which he would grow no more, he was the largest fresh-water fish of any species in Britain, thus fulfilling the promise of his early years. And he became famous. An enclosed lake, unlike a river, is a limited location, and a fish of this size, even in a large pool like Cartench, could not go unnoticed. Andy, who by now had found his school near home, and who had become a fine carp angler, with a number of fish of over twenty pounds to his credit, stalked him uselessly year after year, and knew of his great size, but never talked. But others did, and the tales grew faster than Cypry. People from all over the country came to watch this super-fish, and to try to catch him. Expert anglers of all ages, most seeing nothing of the beauty of their surroundings, attracted mainly by thoughts of the fame, satisfaction, and even money if they were to catch this greatest of all records, congregated on the banks of the lake, while the finances of the local angling club prospered. There were times when Andy felt sick with the certainty that one or other of these famous and skilful men would catch his fish, but they all failed. Soon, Cypry was labelled uncatchable, the beaten anglers departed resigned or angry according to their dispositions but Andy was always there, aware that Cypry had learned more than he, but still hopeful that one day the fish might make a mistake.

Many were the stories told of Cypry's legendary cunning. He had been seen to approach a bait eighty times in a day yet never take it; he had swum monotonously round a floating crust for an hour or more, eventually batting it under with his wide tail, to inspect it contemptuously under water as it rose slowly to the surface. He had knocked over a young lad who was wading in the water to recover a lost float, and he had taken many baits, smashed lines and rods, and generally behaved as a ferocious monster of the deep, if the anglers' stories were to be believed. Nationally-known anglers, white and shaken, were supposed to have quickly removed their baits from the water at the coming of this huge fish, for fear that they would have been unable to land such a leviathan even if they had hooked it. All of these stories were largely untrue, except for those concerning the reactions to a baited hook. As with many experienced carp, Cypry had learnt very great caution towards food, and he had indeed examined both bottom fished and floating baits in the manner reported, in the way of huge carp. Never again would he suck in a normal bait, but he did after all make one more mistake in his life, one which, though understandable, almost resulted in disaster—for record fish once caught, often die from the constant handling they receive.

15 Record

Lon Gurd 1985.

It was sunset and Cypry was on the move. The record carp had
been lying all day in the warm water near the lake centre,
turning occasionally in his own length, his huge mirror scales
catching the sun, the admiration of all the futile anglers on the
bank focused on his great body. Over twenty years of observation had taught him that as the light intensity began to decrease,
the people started to leave, and he could prepare to visit his
secret feeding places. Over ten years had gone by since he had
last been hooked. He had been a twenty pound stripling then,
but had never forgotten that big luscious-looking potato which
he had swallowed in an incautious moment. Since then, he had
rarely eaten anything larger than a fresh-water snail an eighth
of an inch in diameter—the big object which had pulled at
his mouth could not get into one of those, he was quite sure.

One day a Keen Specimen Hunter—a name given to an angler
so fanatical in his pursuit of big fish that he is prepared to spend
any length of time not catching them—appeared on the bank,
complete with floppy hat, numerous badges and an air of
marked superiority. He had a rod which he had built specially

to stop a record fish before it reached the snags; a rod which was as powerful as those used to hurl enormous weights into the far breakers at the seashore. With it went a big fixed spool sea reel loaded with two hundred yards of the best and strongest 30 lbs. breaking strain nylon monofilament line which money could buy. No one who saw him on the day of his appearance in his full regalia would have guessed that he had already spent every day for the past three weeks at the water, disguised as an average angler, but this was all part of his great project ; to catch Cypry, the record carp.

Through his powerful binoculars he had watched Cypry cruising in the middle of the lake and at each sighting his eyes had gleamed behind his adjustable polarizing spectacles. On the quieter weekdays he had abandoned his average angler role, and had charted the lake bed, noting the location of every snag. He had waded the shallows in thigh boots, pinpointing the position of the extensive beds of snails which he had been told were almost the sole food of the big carp. It had not taken him long to see that Cypry never fed during the day and by creeping down rodless at twilight, he had on several occasions seen Cypry moving in after the anglers had gone—moving in to the snail beds, he knew, for his nightly feed. Eventually he spent three whole illegal nights by the lake, walking round the shallow ends, sometimes spotting the enormous movements of Cypry on the feed. The great carp was always alone, as if his bulk caused others to avoid him. At last he selected his pitch —a prolific snail area, where he had watched his quarry feeding night after night at about the same time. It was a bare twenty feet from the water's edge, and the angler would have to set up his rods amid an apparently impenetrable tangle of waterside bushes, where nobody but a carp angler would ordinarily dream of fishing. This just suited him as once he had unobtrusively cleared sufficient space to sit and strike, he would be invisible not only to the fish, but to anyone on the bank only a few feet away.

He went over every aspect of his plan in his motor caravan, specially bought for this trip, the night after he had put phase two into operation, and found the prospect good. He had studied every facet of the scheme and he was certain that he would catch Cypry on the first night of phase three after he had spent the next week fishing assiduously and uselessly all day, and leaving the water every night at the correct time.

He had even studied Bert, the bailiff. He knew that Bert was hard on those who would break the rules. He was not an educated man like the Keen Specimen Hunter, but he had the cunning of fifty years' experience in the woods and by the water, and was not to be underestimated. The last time he had found two anglers night fishing they had been permanently expelled from the club, which had nearly every good water for miles around, so it was stick to the rules, or else, at this water. But he had nothing to lose, for these were not his waters, and anyway he was confident enough that he could outwit the old chap. He had discreetly followed Bert on several evenings, and watched him circle the lake after all the anglers had left, then clump up the rough track to his little cottage, half a mile away in the village from which he never seemed to emerge until the next morning, except for an occasional visit to the pub.

What the KSH didn't know was that Bert had studied him, too. Often during the day the bailiff would move silently through the wood to stand invisible behind a tree, watching. Twice he saw the angler wading about in the lake, probing the bottom, casting a plummet into the water and writing on what appeared to be a map. Now Bert knew that average anglers did not behave in this way, so he was suspicious. Here was a man, he thought, who was going to break the rules one day, and who was, therefore, an enemy; so Bert made his plans, too.

Unless you are an expert actor, it is hard to disguise the way you walk, and it was in this way that the bailiff had recognized the Keen Specimen Hunter the moment he had seen him in his normal fishing clothes, and had slipped out of his house with his powerful torch after the angler had retired one night, found the prepared pitch, guessed what was going to happen, and prepared his own position nearby for what he knew might be a long vigil. Well hidden under the bushes he deposited a certain lengthy object which he planned to use after the KSH had hooked his fish. Every night during the next week the angler packed up his tackle exactly half an hour after sunset, said a virtuous and cheerful goodnight to the bailiff and trudged up to his caravan. Every night Bert disappeared into his cottage, but a few minutes later slipped out of the back door, walked his poacher's walk to his hiding place, and waited in vain until iong after midnight. He had no doubts, however—his time would come.

On the eighth day the KSH was sure he had allayed any suspicions Bert might have had and was ready for phase three, the night he had planned for more than a month, the session that would make *him* the holder of the British Carp Record. That evening he left the water as usual, hurried to the caravan to leave his tackle, crept across a couple of fields, and stationed himself within sight of the door of Bert's old cottage. Soon the bailiff clumped stolidly by, entered the house and shut the door. The angler moved quickly now, back to prepare his tackle for the great night—while Bert was leaving by the back door as usual. By the time the KSH was approaching the pitch with his gear, Bert was in position.

It was almost dark and warm with just a little more wind than the angler had hoped. His two rods were ready, and attached to the end of each line was his secret weapon, the ultimate deception to defeat even Cypry's acute senses. He had had two hooks made of special high-tensile steel wire, no larger than a normal carp hook but much thicker and several times stronger, while welded to every part of the hooks, except the barbs and long, needle-sharp points, were exact replicas of the tiny water snails. They had been treated with a concentrated extract of crushed snail shells, which made them appear, and smell, like the real thing. They would not crush, of course, being of metal, but he intended to strike instantly they were picked up before Cypry had time to discover his mistake, although he had no reason anyway to be suspicious on the snail beds, at night. He arranged the rods in their rests, released the pick-ups, and waded cautiously into the water, holding the 'baits', which he placed about six feet apart on the bottom, among the snails. Then he returned circuitously to the bank, attached a silver paper indicator to each line—no electric bite alarms, as he did not want the noise of the buzzer—and looked around him. All was quiet except for the wind in the trees and the distant call of a hunting owl. The black lake stared at him and he stared back. He was ready, apart for the last ritual act. Glancing quickly at the stars, he made a low bow in the direction of the home of the holder of the present carp record—soon to be the ex-holder, he thought with some satisfaction—a habit of his, and of many really keen specimen hunters before an important fishing session.

Then he placed the big landing net, with its five foot fibre glass arms, close to his hand, made sure the big torch, lashed to its pointed stick, was firmly in the ground pointing towards where the rod tip would be when he hooked the fish, and settled into his bed chair. Now there was only waiting left, and he was good at waiting. So was Bert, fifteen feet away in the bushes. Soon, disturbances in the water indicated that fish were on the feed and there were splashes near the baits. The angler made no movement; these were small fish. Shortly after midnight, the water nearby went very quiet, then a huge swirl showed that Cypry had arrived. The Keen Specimen Hunter concentrated, his eyes fixed on the silver paper blurs, his hands creeping close to the rods. The indicators quivered at times, as eddies from the feeding fish moved the line, but it was half an hour before Cypry took the bait on the left hand rod, and the silver paper cylinder attached to the line moved jerkily towards the butt. The KSH quietly engaged the pick-up, saw the line still going, and hit the fish with all his strength. He was on, as the angler had always known he would be, the rod was bent and vibrating as Cypry moved off, not fast, but with enormous, almost frightening power, towards the nearest snag. The angler let him go for a minute, against the full bend of the special rod, then switched on the big torch, careless now of light or sound. The beam illuminated the heavy line, showing that Cypry was going hard to the left. The KSH knew exactly where the nearest branches in the water were, and at the right time he brought the rod down, and put on full sidestrain. The rod bent until the glass inside the butt creaked under the pressure, but no carp living could stand that pull, and Cypry turned, heading away from the bank. He was beaten and he knew it, and fifteen minutes later the KSH knew it too, as the big net went towards the rolling carp.

It was then that Bert acted. Torchlight flashed for an instant on a wicked-looking curved blade, and the line went slack— Bert had reached through the bushes and cut the line with his weed cutter on its fifteen foot pole, which he had secreted for this very purpose!

With a roar of rage and despair, the normally impassive Keen Specimen Hunter launched himself bodily into the water to grab at the disappearing line, but it was too late. Feeling the release of tension, Cypry had already moved out of reach into the darkness, By the time the angler had scrambled miserably from the lake, tears of frustration mingling with the lake water on his cheeks, Bert was halfway back to the warmth of his cottage, muttering to himself that no one was going to catch *his* carp by breaking the rules.

The Keen Specimen Hunter, keen no longer, departed sadly after finding the discarded weed cutter, and knowing that he would not catch Bert, or the great carp.

And Cypry? He is still there, but he is an old fish, and is losing weight, as he hardly feeds at all now.

The bailiff told Andy the whole story next day, in such a droll way that he could not fail to laugh, in spite of his anxiety for Cypry. It would not take Cypry long to rid himself of the hook by constantly rubbing it against a sunken piece of wood or a rock, but Andy, although glad that the poacher's plan had been foiled by the vigilance and cunning of his friend the bailiff, could not help worrying about whether the carp was damaged in any other way. He need not have worried. Cypry had been exhausted, it was true, and puzzled by the line hanging from his mouth, until he rid himself of the big hook, but once it was gone, and the place in his mouth was healed, he was soon back to normal.

He was never to be hooked again.

16 Immortality?

More than ten thousand times had the earth turned about its axis presenting the gleaming mirror of Cartench Lake to the waiting, distant furnace that was the life-giving sun, but the time of Cypry's death was not yet. The true life span of the great mirror carp, king of all the fresh-water fishes, is not known, nor ever will be. The mortality of the fish was in no doubt, although it seemed always to have been, moving majestically through the ancient lake as if it had no doubts of its own immortality, whatever else around it decayed and died. Fish and water insects, men and animals, birds and all the myriad creatures of the countryside had perished, yet the carp lived on, indestructable, immutable, everlasting. Only the tall trees outlived it.

So thought Andy, although he knew within himself that his thoughts were not logical, as he stood staring into the water one evening a week after Cypry's near capture. He was middle-aged himself now, but still as great a lover of the lake as when he had first fished it, so long ago. Failure to catch the one fish he wanted most had not soured him, for he had come to the realization that it was not that one carp, but the essential unity of the teeming life of lake and wood that mattered most to him. Although he was aware that the huge carp was old, powerful no longer, a failing monarch, he liked to imagine that Cypry's survival for so long since he had watched its tumultuous conception typified his own and every sentient creature's struggle to retain its identity through the constant tribulations of life.

As he turned away, an enormous swirl in the lake centre grew and grew as Cypry, still ever-present, greeted the coming night with his customary near leap, before disappearing again into the enigmatic depths which he had made his own.

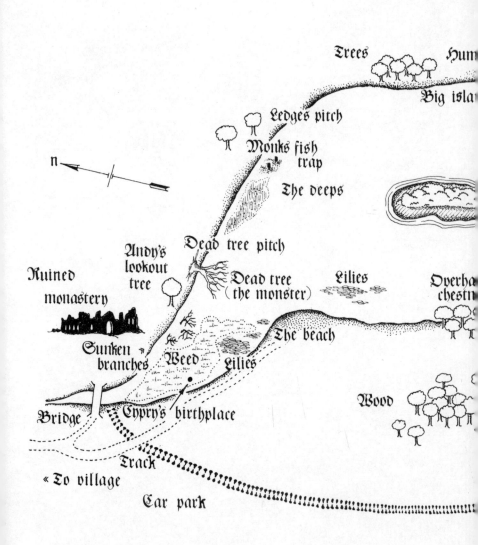

Cartench La[ke]

Trees   Hum

Big isla

Ledges pitch

Monks fish
trap

The deeps

n

Andy's
lookout
tree

Dead tree pitch

Ruined
monastery

Dead tree
(the monster)

Lilies

Overha
chestn

Sunken
branches   Weed

The beach

Lilies

Wood

Bridge   Cypry's birthplace

Track

« To village

Car park